Global Health

Global Health

An Anthropological Perspective

Merrill Singer

University of Connecticut

Pamela I. Erickson

University of Connecticut

Long Grove, Illinois

For information about this book, contact:
Waveland Press, Inc.
4180 IL Route 83, Suite 101
Long Grove, IL 60047-9580
(847) 634-0081
info@waveland.com
www.waveland.com

10-digit ISBN 1-57766-906-1
13-digit ISBN 978-1-57766-906-7

Printed in the United States of America

7 6 5 4 3 2 1

Contents

Preface

This book is a student-oriented tool for learning about global health issues from an anthropological perspective. Anthropology has long been recognized as a discipline that provides in-depth, holistic, context-sensitive, and integrated accounts of diverse peoples and ways of life. It has been referred to as a field of study and applied work that addresses big issues in small places. The places of concern to anthropology are everywhere that humans dwell. As Thomas Eriksen puts it, they range "from the skyscrapers of Manhattan to mud huts in the Sahel; from villages in the New Guinea highlands to African cities" (2001:1). Anthropologists engage in detailed study of the important features of local places, peoples, and social relationships.

At the same time, anthropologists are concerned about the big issues confronting humanity. In the twenty-first century, we inhabit a world in which "no part of the planet is too remote, too exotic, or too forbidding for travelers or business development" (Garrett 2001:12). We all now inhabit (although not equally so) a social environment shaped by rapid global communication; the swift movement of far-flung peoples, ideas, and commodities; and the entanglement of all communities around the planet in a common world economic system. All peoples in their own ways now confront common issues like climate change, degraded environments, loss of biodiversity, urbanization, rising costs, war, and global health threats. How to solve these pressing problems of humanity raises big questions that anthropology seeks to address by *situating the local in the global* and by uniting careful on-the-ground ethnographic research with a holistic examination of global forces and processes. Anthropology has a commitment to human well-being, especially to improving the lives of the poor and marginalized. As Franz Boas, the father of American anthropology, noted, "A knowledge of anthropology enables us to look with greater freedom at the problems confronting our civilization" (1928:7).

Acknowledgments

We want to thank our many students, graduate and undergraduate, over the years. They have kept us working hard to seek ways to reveal the fundamental importance of global health and its complex connections to often unjust structures of human social relationships, a human mediated physical environment, human and other biologies, and the illusive but telling patterns of culture. As well, we thank the many people who have participated in our health research in several countries around the world, sharing with us, their insights, their heartfelt concerns, and, at times, their suffering. We also want to acknowledge and express appreciation for the significant help, good humor, and easy-to-work with styles of Jeni Ogilvie and Thomas Curtin from Waveland Press.

Chapter One

Global Health and the Anthropological Paradigm

We begin this chapter by introducing contemporary threats to global health and provide a brief history of the field of global health as it has evolved from interests in tropical medicine during colonial times to its present form. Next, we point out the goals of global health. Of considerable importance to understanding the field of global health is an awareness of the key players—the institutions, organizations, and agents of global health programming—and the philosophical perspectives that have shaped efforts intended to improve the health and well-being of the planet's human populations. Another key factor for understanding global health is the interplay between health and human rights. Central to global health issues are the social determinants of health and sickness, including the creation and maintenance of the wrenching health inequalities that characterize the contemporary "global community." We identify gaps in our understanding of global health issues and how these impact health and health experience in the contemporary world. We discuss changes in our **human habitat**, that is, our social, political, and ecological worlds that have accompanied the evolution of global health. The chapter ends with a detailed explanation of the anthropological approach and the advantages of using it to understand and address issues of global health.

THREATS TO GLOBAL HEALTH

In the 1990s, awareness of the impact of **globalization** shifted the focus to **global health**, which addresses "the health needs of the people of the whole planet above the concerns of particular nations" (Brown et al. 2006:62). The idea is that health issues now transcend national borders and create a "shared susceptibility to, experience of, and responsibility for health" that will be best addressed by cooperation among nations (Birn et al. 2009:6). Thus, there emerged a new way of thinking about and responding to the transnational health issues of human populations around the globe.

What are the pressing health issues in the world today? While there has been important progress on some indicators of global health, such as infant mortality and life expectancy, we still live in a world in which:

- More than eight thousand babies die every day before they are four weeks old.
- Almost 1.5 million children die of diarrheal diseases annually.
- Almost 287,000 women die in childbirth every year.
- More than 140,000 children die every year of measles.
- Over 1.4 million people die every year of tuberculosis (TB).
- In 2010 malaria infected 216 million people, killing 655,000.

Most of these threats to life are preventable and/or treatable, but they are not being adequately addressed and lead to disturbing disparities in health among regions of the world and subgroups of people. UNICEF reports that 26,500–30,000 children die every day because of poverty. They "die quietly in some of the poorest villages on earth, far removed from the scrutiny and the conscience of the world. Being meek and weak in life makes these dying multitudes even more invisible in death" (UNICEF 2000).

New threats to health include both reemergent and emergent infectious diseases as well as ever more prevalent chronic conditions (e.g., asthma, allergies, cancer, diabetes), a global water shortage, and a world food crisis. These threats are caused and exacerbated by the environmental changes wrought by global warming and other anthropogenic (human-caused) degradations of the environment (e.g., toxic emissions) and have now become substantial factors in human health and disease. Other dangers lurk and threaten to reverse the health improvements that have been made, especially in poor countries. For example, 40 new diseases have been identified since the 1970s, and in recent years alone, WHO has verified over 1,100 epidemic events worldwide. Moreover, WHO points out:

> The poorest of the poor, around the world, have the worst health. Those at the bottom of the distribution of global and national wealth, those marginalized and excluded within countries, and countries themselves disadvantaged by historical exploitation and persistent inequity in global institutions of power and policy-making present an urgent moral and practical focus for action. (2008:31)

A CONCEPTUAL JOURNEY

Where did the global health agenda come from? This question is important not only for historical reasons but also for conceptual ones. It is imperative to understand how the field of global health came to frame its particular understanding of health in the world. In everyday usage, when we talk about health, we often mean "individual health" (e.g., "Sarah has a sore throat."). Global health, by contrast, focuses on the epidemiological idea of **population health** and seeks to measure and compare the population health status of the nations and regions of the world using various morbidity and mortality indicators. "Population health" provides the conceptual framework for thinking about why some populations are healthier than others. It calls attention to the influential role of social and economic forces in combination with biological and environmental factors that shape the health of entire populations (e.g., adolescents worldwide, inhabitants of Nigeria, poor African Americans in New Orleans, women in Amazonia). Population health focuses on (1) the interrelated social and environmental conditions and social forces and trends that influence the health of populations over the life course and (2) identifying systematic variations in patterns of disease occurrence. It uses this knowledge to develop and implement health-related policies and programs designed to improve the health and well-being of populations of concern.

Tropical Medicine Era

Historically, population health emerged from the field of tropical medicine, itself a historic product of the eighteenth- and nineteenth-century European colonial encounter with the indigenous peoples of Africa, Asia, the Americas, and the Pacific Islands. Inherent in colonialism was an agenda of improving local on-the-ground conditions in colonial areas that facilitated the political and economic control of indigenous populations, their labor, and the natural resources of their homeland. Tropical medicine was intended to control local diseases that could hinder the extraction of colonial wealth. Disease was a major problem for Europeans in the tropics. West Africa, for example, was known in Britain as the "white man's grave." Consequently, the initial objective of tropical medicine was protecting the health of European colonial administrators, traders, missionaries, and travelers from the assumed harmful effects of living both in a hot tropical environment and among indigenous inhabitants, usually peoples of color, who were believed to be unhygienic, immoral, and diseased.

One way of achieving the protection of colonial administrators and colonists and thereby promoting the colonial enterprise was "cleansing their newly acquired [territories], attempting to purify not only [their] public spaces, water, and food, but the bodies and conduct of the inhabitants" (Anderson 2006:1). The underlying imperialist ideology embedded in tropical medicine was the sense that medicine and health had a vital role to play in making the world safe for Europeans so that they might carry out their "burden" of ruling over and "civilizing" subordinated peoples and diminishing the innate propensity of these peoples and their environments to spread disease. Two of the most important targeted diseases were malaria and yellow fever, both of which took a tremendous toll on both the colonizers and the colonized.

The London School of Tropical Medicine founded in 1899 (known as the London School of Tropical Hygiene and Medicine after 1924) may be the most famous of the institutes devoted to infectious diseases. Medical researchers, physicians, nurses, and sanitary engineers were the primary personnel working toward better health (primarily for colonizers) in the colonies at this time. As advances in immunization and other disease-control methods became available, these benefits were extended to indigenous populations as gestures of good will that also advanced capitalism. As this historic tale reveals, public health is almost always very political, reflecting as much relationships among people as it does relations with nature or with disease.

International Health Era

By the late nineteenth and early twentieth centuries, with the slow but not yet fully accomplished demise of colonialism, tropical medicine gave birth to the idea of "international health." While tropical medicine, whose concern was the special health problems of tropical regions, did not disappear, increasingly there was a concern for understanding and controlling the specific health problems that plagued the inhabitants of the different countries or regions of the world. In Western countries, initially, the term **international health** came to refer primarily to health practices, policies, and systems in developing nations, rather than to those in developed nations, and stressed the differences between countries more than their commonalities. Additionally, international health focused on bilateral foreign aid activities (e.g., USAID), rather than a collective international action, to control disease in the poor countries of the world, and favored medical missionary work (primarily Christian) in such countries.

As developed countries continued to extract raw materials from less developed countries even as the colonies were beginning to gain independence, private nonprofit foundations concerned with international health issues, such as the Rockefeller Foundation (founded in 1913), Save the Children (a war relief agency founded in 1919), and the Red Cross Societies began to address health internationally. The 1920s saw the establishment of the League of Nations Health Organization (LNHO). The LNHO began to collect, standardize, and disseminate vital and health statistics from around the world. Its publication, the *Weekly Epidemiological Record*, later continued by WHO, included information on infectious diseases, nutrition, social causes of morbidity and mortality, and chronic diseases. It was also at this time that private foundations, particularly the Rockefeller Foundation, began to work with the LNHO, a precedent that continues to this day. The outbreak of World War II (1939–1945) stopped most of these cooperative efforts, except for those directly related to the military. The United States was involved with the development and distribution of sulfonamides and penicillin to Allied forces. After the war, organizations that cover three key categories of assistance were established to address the continuing concerns of the industrialized nations about health and economic development in the less developed countries: (1) WHO, a *global health* organization within the United Nations (UN), (2) the International Monetary Fund (IMF), the World Bank (International Bank for Reconstruction and Development [IBRD]), and other multilateral *financial institutions*, and (3) *bilateral aid and development* organizations (e.g., US Agency for International Development [USAID]) based primarily in the developed countries. Other players included the big pharmaceutical companies, health insurance industries, private philanthropies, and many nongovernmental organizations (NGOs) (Birn et al. 2009). The stated goal of these organizations was to address issues of hunger, disease, and economic development. Yet, it should come as no surprise that the power structure reflected the goals and values of the industrialized nations and continues to do so today. Indeed, an important driver of international development programs at this time was concern about lesser developed countries turning to communism (as had happened in China) and slipping out of the capitalist world system.

Despite these factors, the field of international health really came into its own during this period (1950s–1980s). WHO was an organization with member states that could set health policy and target priorities for bettering health, particularly in the developing nations. WHO defined health as “a state of complete physical, mental and social well-being not merely the absence of disease or infirmity” (Constitution of the World Health Organization 2006:1) and its mission was “the attainment by all peoples of the highest possible level of health." The primary focus of efforts in international health became the control or even elimination of the major scourges of the developing countries—infectious diseases and malnutrition—and improving child health, reproductive health, and water and sanitation conditions.

Eradication of small pox in 1980 is arguably one of the major achievements of WHO with respect to infectious diseases. Attempts to eradicate malaria were initially also very effective due to the use of the pesticide DDT but suffered major setbacks after DDT was banned because of the damage it was doing to the environment. The disease since has resurged almost everywhere, especially in sub-Saharan Africa. WHO's efforts to provide universal immunization against diphtheria, pertussis, tetanus, measles, polio, and TB through the Expanded Program on Immunization (EPI) have saved countless lives, and its child survival program, GOBI-FFF (growth monitoring, oral rehydration, breastfeeding, immunization, food supplementation, female literacy, and family planning), has made significant impacts. The Essential Drugs Program (EDP) identified some 200–500 vitally important drugs and still makes them accessible and affordable to those in need. The Global AIDS Program, while defending the human rights of people living with AIDS, focused narrowly on the importance of individual behavior change.

Making a culturally meaningful healthy lunch at Enuamanu School, Atiu, Cook Islands. (Julie Park)

In the early years, international health was heavily dominated by biomedicine and, except for water and sanitation projects, focused on narrowly defined programs (vertical or top-down approaches like EPI) and individual patients (stressing personal responsibility for health) rather than the broader social and economic issues that affect health (e.g., poverty, lack of health infrastructure and access to care). In 1978, WHO member nations signed the Alma Ata Declaration that called for health needs to be addressed as a fundamental human right with attention paid to the social origins of disease and advocated for the implementation of primary health care to achieve "health for all by the year 2000" (WHO 1981). This was a direct challenge to the status quo and the biomedical reductionism that had guided WHO to that point. The program, however, was undermined at every turn; by the 1980s, WHO had returned to the former strategy of "selective" primary health care. The tension between the philosophy of health implied in the vertical programs (e.g., malaria control) and the horizontal programs (e.g., primary health care for all), the narrow biomedical concerns about individual and social justice issues, and the retention of the status quo versus a new international economic order have been played and replayed over the history of WHO and, by the 1990s, had divided the organization.

Global Health Era

During the 1990s, the term *global health* was increasingly used to refer to health issues internationally. The use of global health paralleled the new economic term, *global economy,* which recognized the increasing systemic economic globalization of our planet. Global health also reflected a change in perspective that involved a conceptual shift from health issues and concerns between nations and regions to those that transcend national borders, such as socioeconomic class, ethnicity, gender, culture, and pandemics. To put it another way, the shift involved flows of capital, people, diseases, medicines, commodities, ideas, and practices that move relatively freely across our culturally constructed political boundaries. Recognition of the need for a global health perspective grew from the emergence of an awareness of the significance of the processes of "globalization" and global connectedness that increasingly are redefining human social worlds and experiences.

It was also in the 1990s that WHO's budget (formerly donations from member states) had become heavily dependent on extra-budgetary funding over which it had less control, and "by 1990 World Bank health project loans surpassed WHO's budget" (Birn et al. 2009:80). By the mid-1990s the bank was the "largest external funder of health" (over $1 billion) (Birn et al. 2009:82). WHO pushed for redistributive primary health care and attention to the social causes of poor health, but this was contrary to the neoliberal economic policies (i.e., deregulation, privatization, and government downsizing) that have dominated the policies of the World Bank since the 1980s. The less WHO controlled the money spent on international health, the less impact it had on pushing forward its agenda for primary health care and social justice, and the more power the World Bank and related organizations had to set the global health agenda.

New key players in global health emerged in the 1990s. Private philanthropic organizations like the Bill and Melinda Gates Foundation (2000), whose budget has surpassed that of WHO, began to influence funding for global health. Such foundations set their own goals for health programming and spending and are accountable only to their board of directors. With such large budgets, they wield enormous influence in the global health arena. Add to these private foundations the many corporate foundations (e.g., Eli Lilly and Company Foundation, ExxonMobil Foundation), business interests (e.g., health insurance companies, pharmaceutical companies), and public-private partnerships (PPPs, e.g., Roll Back Malaria, Global Alliance for Improved Nutrition) and global health has become a province of organizations that, unlike WHO, are not accountable to any democratic body; instead, their global health policy is guided by their own self-interests. Furthermore, they tend to support short-term vertical programs and sacrifice the broader social justice goals of WHO to profit-making.

The extensive involvement of private entities in global health "is also evidenced by the recent formation of the H-8—WHO, UNICEF, UNFPA, UNAIDS, the World Bank, the GAVI Alliance, the Global Fund, and the Gates Foundation—which now hold meetings, like the G-8, in which private entities wield equivalent decision-making powers to public agencies" (Birn et al. 2009:109). WHO, however, continues to champion health as a human rights issue. Its recent publication, *Closing the Gap in a Generation: Health Equity through Action on the Social Determinants of Health: Final Report of the Commission on Social Determinants of Health,* focuses on the continuing social and economic inequalities that impact global health (WHO 2008).

Paralleling the rise of private and corporate interests in global health was the rise of the NGO. NGOs are private, nonprofit agencies that range from small, local grassroots organizations to large international organizations (e.g., International Planned Parenthood Federation). They include humanitarian organizations (e.g., CARE, Catholic Relief Services), relief groups (e.g., Red Cross), social and human rights organizations (e.g., Doctors Without Borders), developing-country NGOs, health and development think tanks, advocacy groups, university and hospital collaborations, research institutions and alliances, professional membership organizations (e.g., the American Public Health Association), and many smaller group or individual efforts—all of which have a concern for improving global health. By the 1990s NGOs had become the major conduit for funding health initiatives in developing countries, bypassing government health institutions (Birn et al. 2009). The many NGOs often compete with each other for funds, hire local health providers away from national health service organizations, and undercut local planning and decision making. Since NGOs receive most of their funding from the major donors (e.g., World Bank, USAID, private foundations, multinational corporations), they are constrained by the dominant philosophies of those organizations and the same structural lack of accountability to the global citizenry.

Health as a Human Right

During the 1980s and 1990s, global health became characterized by a shift away from nation-state models of governance, cooperation, and decision making toward a more amorphous model in which there is no accountability framework. In this way, global health resembles the global economy. Both lack a structure of accountability to the global citizenry. Furthermore, the last three decades of globalization have seen the fragmentation of health policy, funding, and public accountability structures for global health that have resulted in increased inequity and declining health indicators in most developing countries. This has resulted in increased pressure from WHO, the UN, and many of those involved in global health to treat health as a human rights issue and to recognize that social and economic inequities underlie and are the most important factor in health inequities.

Article 25 of the UN's Universal Declaration of Human Rights (1948) clearly includes health and an adequate standard of living as human rights:

> (1) Everyone has the right to a standard of living adequate for the health and well-being of himself and of his family, including food, clothing, housing and medical care and necessary social services, and the right to security in the event of unemployment, sickness, disability, widowhood, old age or other lack of livelihood in circumstances beyond his control.
>
> (2) Motherhood and childhood are entitled to special care and assistance. All children, whether born in or out of wedlock, shall enjoy the same social protection.

The problem with the neoliberal agenda in global health today and the lack of accountability to the global public is, as Paul Farmer has said, based on an important distinction: "Health care can be considered a commodity to be sold, or it can be considered a basic social right. It cannot comfortably be both at the same time" (2003:175). We need a new system that breaks down disciplinary boundaries; recognizes the contribution of biological, social, economic, and political factors on health; recognizes basic health care as a human right everywhere; and questions the free market model of health care as a commodity rather than a social necessity. This requires a shift from vertical to horizontal global health strategies and a commitment to ending global poverty.

THE MISSION OF GLOBAL HEALTH

Global health can be defined as an interdisciplinary field of public health research, policy, and practice that measures and combats health problems worldwide, by identifying health patterns, defining determinants of health issues, and defining strategies for the alleviation of the global health burden. It places a priority on achieving equity in health across national borders and internal social divisions. Given our current global interconnectedness, the mission of the field of global health is to meet the health needs of all the people on the planet through increased cooperation, coordination, and effort.

Adopting a global health approach focuses health assessment, education, intervention, and policy efforts in a number of ways. First, it draws attention to the emergent integrations of economies and societies that are driven by new technologies (e.g., electronic communication) within the world system, including the impacts of new social relationships and institutions that link formerly separate and distinct localities. For example, the shift among youth worldwide from accepting a marriage that is arranged and not based on the couple being in love to desiring a marriage based on choosing and being in love with one's partner is a consequence of the global youth culture promoted by electronic media (music, film, Internet, Facebook, etc.).

Second, a global perspective on health highlights the global flow of pathogens, toxins, pharmaceuticals, and other commodities (including illicit products, like psychotropic drugs), weapons, and waste materials to new places. Illustrative of this point is the dumping of e-waste (e.g., worn out computers, other electronic communication devices, batteries, etc.) from developed regions in underdeveloped nations. Also of concern is the creation of new occupational spaces along borders between countries (e.g., factories or *maquiladoras* along the Mexico/US border, which sprang up after the passage of the North American Free Trade Agreement) that introduce occupational and environmental health risks. (e.g., abuse of female factory workers by their male supervisors).

Third, there are the health consequences of new social and cultural patterns, such as the massive short- or long-term movement of

Family Health Care Center Tagbilaran City, Bohol Province, Philippines. (Pamela Erickson)

workers to foreign lands in search of employment. In recent years, this migration has become highly gendered as developed regions seek caregivers for their homes, their children, their aged, and their sick. Sex workers (including children) are also in high demand in this global flow of bodies. The international demand for female workers has produced an array of new health issues from the spread of sexually transmitted diseases to the mental health problems produced by disrupted social relationships.

Finally, globalization is an uneven process: in some ways all nations develop similar health challenges (e.g., rising rates of asthma and other chronic diseases globally), while in other ways some nations face new local threats to health. Eastern Mediterranean populations are experiencing expanded threats from schistosomiasis, a chronic illness that can damage internal organs. This disease vector is found in contaminated water associated with water development projects designed and implemented for irrigation purposes. In Mexico newly created jobs refurbishing used car batteries from the US are associated with health problems stemming from exposure to toxic materials. As health patterns and threats change, access to health care remains uneven both among and within nations and regions of the world.

CONTOURS OF GLOBAL HEALTH TODAY

The world we live in is characterized by substantial differences in the quality and longevity of life both within and among nations and regions. Having a meaningful impact on these differences and improving health and well-being is the primary motivation for most people who work in global health. Understanding the nature and causes of health differences across populations begins with differentiating **health disparities** (differences in health) from **health inequities** (inequalities in health). Men and women, for example, have different health profiles, in part, because of anatomical reasons. At the same time, women on average live somewhat longer than men, especially in developed countries. These differences are not a consequence of social inequality among women and men and hence would be labeled health disparities. Additionally, populations may have health differences because of divergent cultural practices. Mark Nichter and Mimi Nichter (1996) report that in Bangladesh, Pakistan, Sri Lanka, and the Philippines many mothers delay seeking treatment for children with measles, which is an important cause of child death in many developing countries, because they fear that treatment keeps heat from leaving the body, slows down the normal progression of the disease, and turns the rash from a skin problem to a life-threatening internal illness. By contrast, many disease patterns and other threats to health reflect underlying social inequalities caused by discrimination, stigmatization, oppression, military activity, and lack of access to needed resources. Anthropologists increasingly refer to these kinds of factors as **structural violence** (Farmer 2009) because like war and interpersonal violence they take a significant toll on human life. Social epidemiologist Nancy Krieger, who studies health inequity, summarizes the importance of social inequalities:

> In a world where 2 of 5 of our planet's 6+ billion people lack sanitation and live on less than $2 a day . . . , where 1 in 5 lack access to clean water and live in extreme poverty on less than $1 a day, and where less than 1% of the world's adult population owns 40% of the world's wealth while 50% owns less than 1% [of the world's wealth], documenting and analyzing the links between impoverishment and population health remain a public health imperative. (2007:658)

This statement pinpoints one of the most important social determinants of both individual and population health, namely control over wealth within and across societies. Krieger further asserts:

> Social inequality kills. It deprives individuals and communities of a healthy start in life, increases their burden of disability and dis-

> ease, and brings early death. Poverty and discrimination, inadequate medical care, and violation of human rights all act as powerful social determinants of who lives and who dies, at what age, and with what degree of suffering. (2005:15)

Health inequalities are inherently unfair and unjust and are increasingly being framed as a human rights issue.

While health inequalities are most notable in comparisons between wealthy and poor countries, significant inequalities characterize subgroups even in wealthy nations. Jack Geiger, a professor at the City University of New York Medical School, points out that "at no time in the history of the United States has the health status of minority populations—African Americans, Native Americans, and, more recently, Hispanics and several Asian subgroups—equaled or even approximated that of white Americans" (2002:417).

Social inequalities in health have multiple expressions, including

- Disproportionate or excess morbidity (i.e., disease and disability rates)
- Disproportionate or excess mortality (i.e. death rates)
- Decreased life expectancy
- Unequal access to health care
- Unequal access to other health-supportive resources (e.g., health insurance, good nutrition, a clean environment)

Historical and contemporary political-economic relations among nations are especially important sources of health inequalities. There are great differences in wealth between the developed and underdeveloped countries of the world, particularly in sub-Saharan Africa, where the annual per capita expenditure on health care in many nations is less than US$10 compared with US$2,000–$4,000 in more-developed countries. This differential is largely a consequence of the heavy debt many nations in sub-Saharan Africa owe to financial institutions in the developed nations; this debt precludes greater health care expenditures. Moreover, poor nations that have fallen into debt by borrowing money to fund development programs are under great pressure from lenders like the World Bank and USAID to limit government spending on health and social welfare programs as a condition of their continued ability to borrow.

It is important to understand the pathways by which structurally shaped life experiences and hardships result in biological (and health) effects in the body. Anthropologist William Dressler (1999, 2011) has been involved for many years in the study of the health impacts of perceived social inequities as mediated by the stress process. Dressler differentiates two types of social stressors with biological impacts: acute and chronic stressors. *Acute stressors* consist of sudden and often unexpected events that adversely alter the fabric of day-to-day social life (e.g., a "natural" disaster such as Hurricane Katrina in 2005 or the Japanese tsunami and nuclear meltdown in 2011) and force individuals into a new set of social circumstances to which they must adjust. *Chronic stressors* are comprised of ongoing problems in achieving emotionally satisfying experiences and fulfilling major social roles that are central to individual identities (e.g., head of family, community member, mother). Under conditions of stress, there is a set of neuroendocrine responses that prepare the body for action (the so-called "fight or fight" responses). In cases of chronic stress, various "readiness" responses, such as heightened blood pressure, never fall back to original levels but rather reset continually to ever-higher levels that ultimately can lead to significant disease (e.g., cardiovascular problems, stroke). This is not, however, simply a biological process, Dressler argues, because symbolic stimuli and cultural systems of meaning are critical to the process.

One type of stress that Dressler (2011) has found to be common among the poor is caused by the experience of relative deprivation associated with frustrated consumer aspirations—in other words, the stress experienced from wanting and culturally valuing things that you cannot have or achieve because of social barriers. This he calls **cultural inconsonance**. Dressler's research suggests that the more closely individuals approximate in their own behaviors the shared expectations of local cultural models, the better their health status and vice versa. In research in Latin America and the West Indies, Dressler (1999) found high blood pressure was associated with cultural inconsonance. Another group of anthropological researchers led by Clarence Gravlee (Gravlee et al. 2005) used a similar approach to examine the association of skin color and blood pressure in Puerto Rico and found that having darker skin (as defined culturally in Puerto Rico) and having lower socioeconomic status interact to produce high blood pressure. Overall, this body of research affirms that the inability of individuals to achieve their culturally constituted life goals has profound adverse health impacts.

CASE STUDY
Diabetes among the Tohono O'odham

There are intense debates among health officials, policy makers, researchers, and others over the causes of health differences across populations. A case in point is the distribution of diabetes (particularly type 2 diabetes), which is an incurable, debilitating, and potentially lethal disease. Diabetes has a disproportionate effect on the poor, people of color, and disadvantaged indigenous peoples around the world. Notably, American Indians have one of the highest rates of type 2 diabetes. The indigenous Tohono O'odham people of the

Sonoran Desert of south central Arizona, for example, suffer from more than seven times the US diabetes national average and have the highest known prevalence of diabetes, with 50 percent of the adult population having diabetes (Smith-Morris 2008).

Although diabetes is treatable (e.g., insulin injection, oral medications, dietary controls), people with diabetes are two to four times more likely to develop heart disease or have a stroke, and three times more likely to die of complications from influenza (including H1N1) or pneumonia than nonsufferers. Blindness, amputations, and kidney failure are common in the late stages of the disease, resulting in a reduced life expectancy of five to ten years on average. As a result, diabetes has had a pronounced impact on the lives and life experiences of the O'odham people.

Some researchers believe that the O'odham may be genetically predisposed to diabetes, which, combined with a poor diet and lack of adequate exercise, have led to high rates of the disease. Other researchers, however, point out that diabetes was virtually nonexistent among the O'odham 100 years ago (when they would have had more or less the same genetic composition as today). At the beginning of the twentieth century, a physician and anthropologist visiting the Gila River Reservation recorded only one case of diabetes. By 1965, there were 558 known cases in a population of about 28,000 people. Today, diabetes cases among the O'odham number in the thousands. What changed in those 100 years that might account for this radical health transformation?

Those who question the genetic explanation argue that while diet and exercise certainly do matter in the development of diabetes, these behaviors must be understood as more than individual decisions or as reflections of personalities. In addition, we must consider the contexts of people's day-to-day lives: what foods are available to them, what is their socioeconomic status, to what degree do they have a sense of control over their lives, what challenges are they facing in the wider world, and what kinds of resources do they have to cope with these challenges at the population and household levels?

In this light, it is noteworthy that the onset of the O'odham diabetes epidemic coincides with the local damming of the Gila River and other rivers for upstream water use by farmers and by the city of Phoenix. The diversion of water from the O'odham reservation destroyed their agriculture and livelihood, plunging them into poverty. Anthropologists like Mariana Ferreira and Gretchen Lang (2006) argue that for groups like the O'odham, the trauma of historical events, combined with continuing inequities in everyday social life relative to the dominant society, produce a chronic stress response. Over time, this bodily response to continued exposure to stress (as opposed to short-term exposure for which our bodies seem well adapted) weakens the body's immune system, heightens blood-sugar levels, and results in the overproduction of adrenaline cortisol and other hormones related to diabetes. From this vantage, the prevalence of diabetes among the O'odham reflects the biological and health consequences of social inequality and structural violence.

THE ANTHROPOLOGICAL APPROACH

Since the beginning of the field in the nineteenth century, anthropologists have reported on health-related features of human social life under varied social, environmental, and economic conditions. Anthropological interest in health and illness gained considerable momentum in response to the rapidly changing health and social conditions that emerged after World War II, when international health became the focus of the newly formed World Health Organization (WHO). From the 1950s to the 1980s the focus was on improving the health of people within individual nations by strengthening their biomedical prevention and treatment capacities.

In this book, we emphasize the anthropological perspective on global health for three reasons. First, because of its ethnographic approach to knowledge generation and its enduring concern with human subjectivities and insider (**emic**) points of view, the anthropological perspective draws attention to what the health statistics alone cannot tell us. It does this by ensuring that people—as experiencing, feeling, and self-aware beings—are not lost in the epidemiological and public health analysis of health statistics, infant mortality rates, or other quantitative measures. For example, while it is important to understand the patterns of diffusion and growing number of cases of an infectious disease like dengue fever (discussed in chapter 3), as well as the role of global economic and climate changes on the spread of this disease, it is also necessary to appreciate how dengue interacts with human experience, local understandings, and culturally shaped behaviors, and how all of these factors influence risk of infection and social response to infection once it occurs.

In the barrio of Villa Francisca in the Dominican Republic, anthropologists Jeannine Coreil, Linda Whiteford, and Diego Salazar (1997:165) found that residents hold generally fatalistic attitudes about dengue, believing that there is not much they as individuals, as families, or as a community can do about it because the environment is beyond their control. This fatalism is based on their lived-experience in their local environment and what they are able and not able to control. This worldview shapes the responses of the people of Villa Francisca to dengue in ways that must be considered in attempting to prevent this widespread, painful, and potentially lethal disease. Another example of the effect of cultural beliefs on health comes from

Northern Nigeria where Renne (2006) found that some parents refused to allow their children to be inoculated against polio because of the belief that the vaccine was contaminated with HIV and antifertility drugs. Notes Vinay Kamat, "Health planners must consider community beliefs and practices when developing and implementing health policies, as communities must be reasonably convinced of their value before they will embrace change" (2009:56). The anthropological approach encourages understanding of "what actually goes on in the household unit" (Mull 2000:323), as well as during conversations at community gatherings, encounters on the plaza, chance meetings in the local marketplace, and in the many other spaces of meaningful human interaction.

The second reason to think about global health anthropologically is that it offers a means of viewing in careful detail the day-to-day health challenges people face in different locations and in diverse cultural contexts. The anthropological perspective equips students with the conceptual tools needed to see beyond dominant assumptions to assess the actual role of local conditions and social experiences in the making of health and sickness. This is important because disease understandings develop at the local level, as do social responses to limit adverse health outcomes through social and cultural adjustments. Medical anthropologists use the term *idiom of distress* to label social awareness of illness symptoms as culturally appropriate behavioral expressions of anguish and anxiety in response to distressing life events. In many parts of Latin America and among Latino populations in the US, for instance, *ataque de nervios* (attack of nerves) is a culturally recognized illness that, rather than constituting evidence of a mental health problem (e.g., a panic disorder) as it sometimes has been interpreted by psychiatry, may serve as a mechanism for culturally approved ventilation of social suffering (Guarnaccia et al. 2010). Awareness of the local acceptance of ataque de nervios as a normal and appropriate reaction to intense distress can avoid miscommunication, misunderstanding, misdiagnosis, and the misallocation of resources in global health programming.

The **anthropological paradigm** therefore offers a useful corrective to the tendency in global health to view both disease and intervention in narrowly medical and technical terms and not to pay sufficient attention to the human elements of cultural beliefs and behaviors in the domain of health. It is critical to consider both the beliefs and the practices of the lay community and those of health care providers as well.

Finally, the anthropological perspective offers a framework for situating the local within political-economic and political-ecological global contexts and processes that include the structural inequalities and adverse world-changing forces of economic globalism and planetary warming. The field of global health is especially concerned with improving health in the poor nations of the world, which tend to have the worst health profiles. Those who embrace the anthropological perspective are concerned that "unreflexive depictions of [local] cultural practices as casual factors" (Craddock 2004:3) often mean that victims are blamed for inadequate outcomes of health measures. Karen Moland and Astrid Blystand say that "the close attention anthropology can give to people's practical lives and their experiences generates substantial knowledge of the political-economic, and by extension, the moral-ethical dimensions of the topic at hand" (2009:475). Anthropology recognizes the importance of investigating the social embeddedness of disease vulnerability as a determinant of the health. This pathway often leads beyond dominant viewpoints, established epidemiological conceptions, and prevailing "top-down" models of health intervention to new ways of understanding and new, community-driven and participatory strategies of health promotion.

As a biocultural discipline, anthropology focuses on the ways that culture and biology interact. Contemporary research suggests that our health—even our biology—can be significantly influenced by stress, and the stress of enduring injustice and social subordination is often reflected in the body's ailments (Galhardo et al. 2007). Research by Janet Rich-Edwards, Nancy Krieger and their colleagues (2001) found that chronic stress intensifies the risk of preterm delivery by raising levels of placental corticotropin-releasing hormone (CRH). Women who have been the targets of racism or interpersonal violence may be at special risk of preterm delivery and its attendant health challenges for newborns. Similarly, anthropogenic climate change and its consequences, such as an increase in the frequency of extreme weather, can be especially harsh on health in low-income communities and nations that lack the resources to respond quickly or effectively to climate-related disasters. The World Bank (2012) defines low-income countries as those with gross national income per capita of under $1,025 in 2011. Even developed countries lack appropriate resources to deal with, severe storms. In the United States in 2005, Hurricane Katrina stretched our capacity to respond with timely and adequate disaster relief, and those who suffered most were the poor, the elderly, and people of color.

Global climate change and other forms of anthropogenic environmental degradation and their causes, effects, and amelioration are intimately related to culture (Crate 2009). Health is strongly affected by the environment in which we live and by the many ways culture, society, and global political-economic systems interface with that environment (Baer and Singer 2009; Nichter 2008). Complex links intertwine biology and culture, the local and the global, developed and underdeveloped nations, and human societies and the physical worlds they inhabit. Medical anthropologists have long recognized the multiple levels, from individual to global, that affect health and illness. Understanding the complexity of global health issues is essential to addressing them. Anthropology can help us learn to form a creative and holistic vision for improving global health.

An anthropological paradigm reveals that while great strides have been made in improving the health of many people around the world over the last 60 years, human impacts on the environment, violent social conflict, and increasing social inequality are diminishing the success of global health initiatives and threaten to reverse them completely in many areas. These "adverse forces in health" impede efforts to reduce global human social and physical suffering. Hundreds of millions of people, as a result, especially those living in low- and middle-income countries, but the poor of wealthy countries as well, continue to become ill, to be disabled by, or to perish from preventable or treatable diseases. In many countries, nutrition and the health of the poor have improved only slowly. In others they have declined as a result of the HIV/AIDS pandemic. Enormous inequalities in health status and access to health services prevail within and across nations.

CONCLUSION

Health is more than an individual matter. Who we are, where we live, what resources are available to us, how we are treated in society, how equitable our societies are, how clean our environments are, the state of our living and working conditions, and how much control we have over our lives all matter a great deal. There is a growing literature documenting the deleterious effects on health of extreme inequities in wealth and feelings of relative deprivation. Systemic and persistent health disparities are everywhere linked to underlying inequalities in power and resources, and these are political issues that need to be considered in global health policy (Birn et al. 2009). A major goal of this book is to provide readers with the skills to understand these complex issues and to think about realistic solutions within a critical, holistic, and culturally informed anthropological framework.

Chapter Two

The Importance of Culture in Health

Anthropologists mean something very specific when they talk about culture. Edward Tylor (1871:1), one of the earliest scholars to call himself an anthropologist, defined culture as "that complex whole which includes knowledge, belief, art, law, morals, custom, and any other capabilities and habits acquired by man [and woman] as a member of society." (Tylor 1871). It is what people learn to believe about the natural and supernatural world and our place in it, how we should make our living, and how we should behave. Culture, in this sense, is the primary means humans use to cope with changing local, national, and global challenges and opportunities in the world; human nature is cultural as a consequence of our evolutionary history.

Anthropologists also, historically, have used the term **culture** to label specific configurations of the human capacity to encounter and experience the world through a constructed set of shared beliefs, values, norms, emotions, and behavioral patterns. In this sense, anthropologists have talked about similarities and differences between, for example, the Nuer and the Dinka of south Sudan and western Ethiopia in East Africa (Evans-Prichard 1940). Although individual "cultures" like these two are different (i.e., uniquely patterned) and always changing, a core set of beliefs and values tends to persist within each over time, distinguishing one culture from the other. Other examples of distinctive cultural patterns include individualism and hard work as core values in American culture, the idea of karma and rebirth in India, and the importance of harmony with nature among many indigenous peoples worldwide (e.g., Native Americans and First Nations in North America). These kinds of core patterns may persist for centuries amidst continual change of other sorts (e.g., the development of India as a complex modernizing society in a globalizing world). Cultural anthropologists traditionally have studied the diversity of human cultures over time and space and attempted to understand mechanisms of culture change and stability.

Culture is a pervasive force in our lives, but, because it is changing and dynamic, it is not narrowly prescriptive of our individual behavior or experience. As a consequence, in recent years, many anthropologists have wondered whether, in using terms like Japanese culture or Hopi culture, we turn observable but usually flexible and internally varied ways of living into fixed and frozen entities. Still, it is hard to get away from the concept of culture as fixed because we know that members of a group or society (to varying degrees) share key elements of that core set of values and they use these as a processual template for living in the world as they know it. This template we call *culture* arranges our social relationships—Who counts as kin? What is the role of parents, children, and others in our lives? What are the roles of men and women in society? What kind of marriage is appropriate? What are the appropriate arrangements for sex and reproduction?—and the broad outline of our lives—what we eat, what we do, what we believe, and what we think. It also provides our lives with meaning, purpose, and order, as well as emotional attachments and emotional experiences. Most relevant to health, culture takes our natural biological urges (e.g., need for food, sex, elimination, sleep) and teaches us how to express them in particular ways. It also shapes our ideas about what makes us sick, what makes us well, and what kinds of healers we use and trust in our quest for good health. Anthropologists often use the term **health culture** to refer to the health-related aspects of a cultural system. This is the special domain of a subfield of anthropology known as **medical anthropology**.

As we grow up in a community we learn how to behave in the cultural ways that are characteristic of that community. We are **enculturated** into our own culture from birth through observation, instruction, and modeling. Our culturally constituted world becomes second nature to us. As a result, we experience our group's way of doing things and thinking about the world as natural and as the only right way of behaving, feeling, and thinking. But cultures differ on many of these basic issues because there are many ways to solve the problems of human life, including problems of health and illness.

Every culture develops in a specific geographical location and environment (although cultural elements may diffuse to other areas), and this shapes how we make a living (e.g., hunting, fishing, farming, mining, etc.). How we go about providing the basic necessities of life is especially important to the kind of social organization and belief system that exists within a human society.

Hunter-gatherers, for example, of which there are relatively few today, have different worldviews from horticulturalists, farmers, industrial city dwellers, or postmodern global economic participants. They live in a world in which day-to-day subsistence depends on their own ability to hunt and gather enough food to survive. This usually entails a semi-nomadic lifestyle, temporary dwellings, few possessions, and an animistic belief system that imbues the natural world with supernatural features. Often in such societies, spirits of places or animals, witches, and ghosts are thought to cause disease. Among the Waorani, traditionally a tropical forest hunter-gatherer and horticultural group in the Ecuadorian Amazon with whom one of us (Erickson) has done research, disease and death were not traditionally perceived as natural, but rather were caused by witches or shamans. Stopping disease or redressing a death required retaliation against the witch and often his or her family as well. In sharp contrast, American postindustrial, postmodern culture has a strong belief in the naturalness of disease and death, which are rarely attributed to witches or supernatural forces but rather to natural processes in the physical body that have causes that can be measured, understood, and in many cases treated by our biomedical system. How do anthropologists understand these two very different systems of belief surrounding health and illness?

THE ANTHROPOLOGICAL LENS

We begin by using the **anthropological lens**, a way of seeing the worlds of others by seeking to understand their beliefs, emotions, and behaviors within the context of their overall culture and from the points of view of the members of that culture. Anthropologists call this **cultural relativism**, an approach that does not judge other cultures from the perspective of our own culture (**ethnocentrism**), but an approach that seeks to find the internal logic of other cultural systems and how this is related to the ways people understand their world and their place in it. This, of course, does not mean that the anthropologist necessarily agrees with all tenets of a cultural system, some of which may be ethically or morally abhorrent to her personally (e.g., slavery, genocide). Robert Edgerton (1992), an antirelativist anthropologist, in fact argues that many culturally constituted practices like racism, cannibalism, economic exploitation, corruption, anthropogenic environmental degradation, torture, infanticide, slavery, wife beating, and rape are not adaptive, especially from the standpoint of those who are victimized as a result. He argues there are maladaptive aspects of culture, and these can be the sources of much human suffering.

Still, there are problems with completely abandoning the concept of cultural relativism, especially in contexts in which more powerful societies encounter less powerful ones or dominant groups in a society justify their harsh treatment of others with "cultural rationalizations" (e.g., "they are poor because they don't work hard or value education"). Early contacts between biomedicine and groups that had nonscientific medical systems, for example, tended to lead to physicians and others from the dominant group to judge encountered cultures and their medical beliefs as backward and ignorant, an ethnocentric reaction. Indeed, one of the greatest problems in international health efforts has always been the very different theories embedded in local and biomedical understandings of disease and disease processes. The global eradication of smallpox, for example, was a very difficult campaign, in part, because cultures have differing ideas of its cause; some attribute it to the supernatural realm rather than to a virus that can be passed from one person to another. In some parts of India, smallpox was thought to be caused by a visitation from a goddess named Sîtalâ and vaccination was believed to interfere with this divine being, inviting her wrath. Thus, it is not surprising that people fled from the vaccinators; they thought the goddess would be angry and make things even worse for them if they interfered with spiritual processes. Imagine how fruitless it would be to try to convince Americans that Sîtalâ and not a virus causes smallpox and you begin to see how embedded in culture our health beliefs are.

One of the best contemporary books about cultural and medical misunderstandings is Fadiman's (1997) *The Spirit Catches You and You Fall Down*, which chronicles the tragic interactions and misunderstandings that occurred during biomedical treatment of a Hmong child, Lia Lee, for epilepsy in Merced, California. For her parents, epileptic seizures signaled that Lia was special and could communicate with the spirit world. Her doctors, by contrast, saw them as life-threatening events that needed to be prevented through medication. The parents' and doctors' ideas about the illness and its treatment could hardly have been more different. Although her parents were terrified by the violence of her seizures, they were ambivalent about biomedical treatment and did not always follow the prescribed medication schedule. The doctors, who focused exclusively on the physical body and ignored or rejected any metaphysical aspects of illness, believed the parents were simply noncompliant with treatment. Although they all wanted the best for Lia, they differed on just what that meant. As a result, Lia continued to have seizures until a grand mal seizure left her in a permanent vegetative state until her death at age 30—a tragic outcome for the doctors, but an accepted circumstance for the Lees. Many applied medical anthropologists focus on such issues of translation between differing understandings of disease.

For medical anthropologists, health, disease, and treatment are more than narrow biological phenomena. How we get sick, why we get sick, our symptoms and illness experience, and what sickness means to us are determined both by the physicality of disease and the social, cultural, political, and economic factors that influence its emergence and expression. The same is true for how we get better and how diseases are understood and handled by health care providers, be they brain surgeons, herbalists, or Reiki masters. Although many medical anthropologists continue to focus on explaining local medical systems, there is recognition that sickness and health cannot be understood solely from a local cultural perspective. Today, most medical anthropologists combine a focus on the local with an effort to understand local interaction with broader political, economic, global, and social frameworks that impact lived-experience. For many medical anthropologists, an issue of primary concern is the role of social inequality in the origin and consequence of disease, as well as in access to treatment. It is well established, for example, that wealthy people tend to be healthier than poor people and that social inequality and health inequality go hand in hand. This is the **critical medical anthropology** (CMA) perspective whose particular anthropological lens we use in this book.

Within this framework, medical anthropologists—both academic and applied—study complex bio-socio-cultural interactions that impact health around the world to understand:

- the nature of health, disease, and illness at the individual (e.g., sufferer experience, illness behavior), community, population, and global levels, as impacted by biological, environmental, social structural, economic, transnational, and cultural factors;
- the development and operation of systems of health knowledge, belief, and practice (i.e., caring/curing) at the professional, folk, and lay levels;
- the health consequences of structures of social inequality;
- the health care and patient/support network relationship (e.g., cultural competence in health care);
- the nature and interaction of biomedicine and alternative medical systems;
- the health and other impacts of biomedicine and its technologies in Western and non-Western settings;
- the ways environmental factors, and human forces on the environment, impact health; and
- the application of research to health/health care improvements.

HEALTH INEQUITIES: STRUCTURAL CAUSES

Recall that *health disparities* refers to measurable difference in health status among different sectors of the population irrespective of the cause of those disparities and that *health inequalities* refers to the disproportionate or excess morbidity, mortality, and decreased life expectancy and access to health care and resources in disadvantaged groups in society or the world at large. Health inequalities point to the underlying social causes of many health disparities. As noted above, it is social inequalities that produce health inequalities, including unequal access to health care and other health-supportive resources, and overexposure to adverse conditions of living. Health inequality has emerged as a major public health issue worldwide both within and between nations and has become increasingly important in critical medical anthropology research.

While there are many theories about why some groups have better health than others (e.g., cultural differences, biological or genetic differences, psychosocial differences, individual lifestyle differences, structural differences), in this book we suggest that it is the *structural* features of societies that are most important. The social structural or critical view holds that health disparities are more than the consequences of individual decisions and actions. They are the products of social inequality in many spheres of life from lack of opportunity for a good education and housing, to experiences of racial profiling, to access to health care. From this perspective, the key issue is not health disparity per se, but social injustice and health inequity.

A critical structural perspective draws attention to the **social determinants of health** (SDH), defined as "the conditions in which people live and work, and that affect their opportunities to lead healthy lives" as well as the underlying structure of social relationships that shapes unequal social environments (Labonté and Schrecker 2007:5). Social structure affects health status indirectly through various psychosocial and psychobiological mechanisms. As discussed in chapter 1, unequal access to resources produces conflict between expectations or desires and achievement that can lead to cultural inconsonance and feelings of relative deprivation compared to others. Discrimination and stigma are also known to impact health through the effects of chronic stress responses in the body.

Epidemiologist Nancy Krieger provides us with a means to understand "how we literally incorporate, biologically, the material and social world in which we live . . ." to the extent that "no aspect of our biology can be understood absent knowledge of history and individual and societal ways of living" (2001:672). Krieger uses the example of hypertension in African Americans to illustrate this idea. Hypertension, she suggests, is the embodiment of lifelong interactions of racial discrimination (i.e., chronic triggering of the fight-or-flight response); segregation and economic deprivation; high–fat, high-sodium, and low-vegetable diets (influenced by local food availability); greater rates of preterm birth that can harm renal development; exposure to hazardous environments in low-income areas (e.g., toxic wastes, lead paint, fumes from freeways and streets); targeted marketing of alcohol, tobacco, and other drugs; and inadequate health care. All of these factors may individually raise the risk of hypertension among African Americans, but, *taken together*, their synergistic effect is much greater. Not surprisingly, resistance to racial oppression among African Americans reduces their risk of hypertension (Krieger 2003:673).

Consider the way in which narrowed opportunity structures limit life options and self-esteem, which may give rise to risky behavior patterns. Discrimination and fear lower morale and can lead to dangerous life choices (e.g., HIV and STI risk behaviors). In addition, risky behaviors themselves may be self-medication for the injuries of oppression (e.g., taking drugs, which can impact the immune system and its capacity to fight disease). Sexual risk behavior has been studied extensively, especially since the advent of HIV/AIDS. Having multiple sexual partners increases the risk of sexually transmitted infections, and poverty environments the world over have been linked to sexual systems that include maintaining different sexual partners as a means of resource access. The authors' recent study of inner-city minority young adults in Hartford, Connecticut, found that both men and women maintained different partners for a variety of reasons including love and companionship, sexual fulfillment, access to their children, access to desired items (e.g., new shoes, a car, jewelry, hair extensions, etc.), and access to basic necessities (housing, food). Often, long-term relationships were maintained with several partners overlapping in time, heightening the risk for STIs (Singer et al. 2006).

Unequal access also impacts diet and nutrition, which is a key contributor to poor health. The concepts of **food deserts** (geographic spaces that have no grocery stores within several miles) and **junk food islands** (high concentrations of fast-food chains and convenience stores) have received much attention as important factors in the obesity epidemic in America. Inner-city environments are particularly poor in sources of fresh fruits and vegetables and unprocessed foods. In addition, healthy foods may be too expensive for many households, thereby limiting individuals' choices to fast-food chains, convenience stores, and liquor stores. These food sources deliver more calories per dollar spent than sources that offer healthier choices.

In short, structural inequality and oppression breed health consequences: "being at the top of the [social class] heap is a lot better than being on the bottom. . . . There has been an explosion of research indicating that social class is a powerful, and arguably the most powerful, predictor of health." (Budrys 2010:195). This model has a long history in social medicine beginning with Engels' 1845 study of the health of the working classes in London and Virchow's nineteenth-century championing of medicine as a social science. Virchow sought to understand how social and economic conditions impact health, disease, and the practice of medicine and to use that understanding to foster a healthier society. Medical anthropologists are particularly well-suited to make contributions concerning the local health impacts of structural features. The authors' edited book series, entitled Advances in Critical Medical Anthropology, is devoted to publishing case studies of the structural impact on health inequities.

STRUCTURAL HEALTH INEQUALITIES: CONTEXTUAL EXPRESSIONS

Human health is significantly impacted by the social and physical contexts in which people live their lives. Some contexts, like cities, are intentionally and culturally built environments (even if many of their features are unintentional, like air pollution). Other contexts, which are sometimes referred to as "natural environments," may not be intentionally built (e.g., the secondary growth forests of New England), but they also reflect a long history of human intentional and unintentional changes (e.g., there are very few forested areas in New England that were not cleared of most trees and farmed during the colonial and postcolonial eras). In other worlds, culture is a significant force in both built and so-called natural environments. Moreover, both of these contexts reflect structures of inequality in human relationships (e.g., wealthy and poor sections of cities, the flight of the middle class from cities to environmentally more pleasing suburban areas). These points are illustrated in the following sections.

Asthma and Obesity

Increasing rates of asthma are related, in part, to air pollution, a socially constructed health risk created by our mode of using fossil fuels, such as coal, petroleum, and natural gas that are high in carbon and release particles into the air. These particles can trigger asthma attacks. Simultaneously, the current obesity epidemic is clearly related to our consumption of processed foods, foods with high-fat and sodium contents, large food portions, and sweetened drinks. Pricing structures of foods make calorie-dense fast-food cost far less than fruits, vegetables, and lean meats. Obesity is also related to poor exer-

Polluting industry in Louisiana. (Merrill Singer)

cise habits, often due to the lack of safe areas in the inner city where people can walk or jog, the suspension of physical education in schools, and the ubiquity of automobiles (Bellisari 2013). The **obesogenic environment** was generated socioculturally over several decades, culminating in the present fact that more than 60 percent of Americans are overweight or obese, placing them at greater risk for heart disease, cancer, diabetes, and musculoskeletal problems. In fact, this is the first generation of American children who are expected to have a lower life expectancy than their parents (*NIH News* 2005). Both asthma and obesity are global health problems and are products of broad cultural-political-economic changes.

Hantavirus

Infectious disease, too, is often the result of human–ecosystem imbalances. A case in point is the 1993 hantavirus outbreak in the Four Corners area—where Arizona, Utah, Colorado, and New Mexico meet. The hantavirus that caused the epidemic was a previously unknown hantavirus (now known as Sin Nombre [Spanish for "without a name"]) that is harbored in various species of mice, western chipmunks, and other rodents. Humans can be infected by inhaling infective saliva or excreta present as aerosols. Infection in adults is usually through domestic, occupational, or leisure activities that bring humans into contact with infected rodents, most often in a rural setting. In the 1993 epidemic most of the patients were Native Americans who had influenza-like symptoms, followed by rapid onset of pulmonary edema with a fatality rate of 52 percent (Simonsen et al. 1995). Notably, Native American elders recognized that the heavy rains in the spring had increased the food supply for rodents, who multiplied. In the past, such conditions were associated with experiencing the disease to the extent that the Navajo believed that mice were the bearers of illness and that healthy young men would become sick and die with an illness that came with the rains. Part empirical observation, part extensive culturally shaped knowledge gained from living in the Southwest's environment, and part oral tradition and wisdom of the ancients—this case illustrates how culture shapes understanding of human–environmental interactions and disease.

HIV/AIDS

HIV/AIDS, now considered a chronic condition in areas with access to treatment, was arguably the most frightening epidemic of the 1980s and 1990s, when the disease became a threat to the health of poor and marginalized populations globally as a result of social conditions. This disease in humans is caused by the HIV retrovirus, which attacks the immune system, leading to its progressive failure, thereby allowing life-threatening opportunistic infections and cancers to thrive. It was first clinically described in 1981 in the United States in a cluster of gay men, with no known cause of impaired immunity, who had symptoms of *Pneumocystis carinii* pneumonia (PCP), a previously rare opportunistic lung infection. Later cases presented with a rare skin cancer called Kaposi's sarcoma (KS). Many more cases of PCP and KS emerged, alerting the US Centers for Disease Control and Prevention (CDC) to the outbreak of a new and frightening disease that, in the early years, was considered fatal.

Cultural explanations of HIV have ranged from condemnation of gay and drug-using lifestyles as causes of the disease to assertion of punishment from God, to naturalistic explanations. In the early years of the epidemic, HIV/AIDS was a highly stigmatized disease in which infection was considered deserved (i.e., gay men, drug users) or undeserved (i.e., innocents infected by blood transfusion or by maternal transmission), depending on the route of infection. Before the cause and routes of infection of HIV were known (exchange of infected body fluids through sex, intravenous drug use, blood transfusion, breast milk, labor and delivery) and the nearly universal susceptibility to infection, HIV was enveloped within a cultural trope of purity and danger. Today, we understand that HIV originated in nonhuman primates in sub-Saharan Africa and was transferred zoonotically to humans late in the nineteenth century or early in the twentieth century, most likely through cultural practices like the hunting and handling of bush meat. In response to population pressure and worsening economic conditions, bush meat became a nutritionally important commodity in poor rural communities and has been traded on a wide scale in western and central Africa.

Mountaintop Removal

A final example of the role of culturally constituted contexts in human health is seen in the style of mining known as mountaintop removal, in which whole mountain tops are blown away to reveal coal seams that are then extracted using large, heavy machinery that strips away the coal instead of mining it underground. Mountaintop removal is particularly common in Appalachia (Kentucky, Virginia, and West Virginia) and in other places as well. It has replaced underground mining because it uses fewer workers and is more profitable. Anthropologist Bryan McNeil (2011) chronicles the history of one coal mining area in West Virginia and shows how globalization, neoliberal polices (i.e., society remade in the image of a specific business ideology of profit and growth without restriction), environmental destruction, and declining health and welfare of local populations are intertwined in a social context of deregulation, union-busting, and government policies supporting "Big Coal."

McNeil argues that coal mining in Appalachia was transformed from an industry in which many local men were employed as miners for companies with relatively small land holdings compared to the large holdings today. Formerly, owners lived in the area, and unionized miners fought long and hard for health and safety benefits. Coal mining became part of the culture of Appalachia as did use of the local mountains for food (hunting and gathering) and recreation.

The new form of mining, however, destroys the environment, impoverishes communities, restricts access to the mountains for recreation and subsistence activities, pollutes the air and water in surrounding areas, causes landslides, and contributes to psychological stress and illness among inhabitants from the constant blasting that shakes their homes, the coal dust that sifts into their dwellings, the pollution of their water sources, the displacement of whole communities, and the numerous accidents caused by overloaded, overweight hauling trucks. The coal companies, now global corporations, are detached from the land and the people, so the destruction is not felt personally at the corporate level.

Although local community activists continue to attempt to curb the excesses perpetrated by Big Coal, they are met with a political system that is in its pocket, an eviscerated labor-union movement, and a sense of powerlessness and despair that affects people's health and well-being. Stripped of both their environment and their way of living—and sometimes even life itself due to harsh mining practices that unleash many kinds of collateral damage on communities—people are left with the decision to stay and fight the owners of the coal companies or leave, as so many already have.

THE EMIC PERSPECTIVE AND SUBJECTIVE EXPERIENCE

The cases discussed above clearly show why it is important to understand the emic perspective, by which we mean the *personal experience* of people who are dealing with the intertwined issues of a deteriorating environment, changing cultural practices, social inequality, and resulting health issues. There has been a strong revival of the principles of social medicine among health professionals, many of whom realize how our changing cultural ways of living on the globe have created serious health problems. Hearing individuals' own experiences of suffering and resistance helps us to understand the threats we face and the means we have to combat them.

Overweight and obese people—the majority of Americans—are discriminated against and blamed for their illness despite the signifi-

The poor diet of a developed nation. (Pamela Erickson)

cant economic and social factors involved. It is not just an individual problem but rather a societal and global problem caused by cultural changes in food production, distribution, and consumption along with the ways we use (or don't use) our bodies anymore in work and play.

Emerging infectious diseases will always be with us. In the wake of global warming and the global flow of commodities (on and in which pathogens are carried), some infectious agents will expand their range into territories where they previously did not exist, causing people in local environments to suffer the consequences. The environmental changes and destruction wrought by our industrial and global economic systems are embodied by all of us in different ways. How people understand disease/illness and its causes is important not only in facilitating meeting health needs on a personal level (e.g., health care seeking) but also in promoting changes that lead to the prevention of conditions that plague all of us in the twenty-first century.

CONCLUSION

An anthropologically informed approach to global health includes both an understanding of the local conditions, experiences, and emic perspectives of people afflicted as well as an understanding of the structural factors that affect the health of individuals, families, and communities worldwide. On the treatment side, it has become increasingly apparent that the great traditions of medicine (Ayurvedic, Traditional Chinese Medicine, Greco-Roman, and Unani), which all promote moderation in food, drink, and exercise as well as a balance of personal, social, environmental, and spiritual forces, give us good advice for a long and healthy life (Erickson 2008). It also has become increasingly clear that health requires balance—in our personal body system, the social system, and the ecosystem—and, as the next chapter argues, a solution to the threats posed by the interaction of environmental destruction and global warming that have resulted from our unsustainable global economic system.

Chapter Three

Environment and Globalization

This chapter examines health in light of our changing and complexly intertwined physical and social environments. It focuses on **global climate change** (also called global warming) and **economic globalization**. Both of these forces have implications for global health in general and for health inequality in particular.

ENVIRONMENTAL HEALTH

Environmental health is a key concept for understanding global health issues. Just what do we mean by *environmental health*? Dutch atmospheric chemist Paul Crutzen (2002) argues that the geographic age of Earth in which we now are living should rightfully be called the Anthropocene Age (Age of People) because of the significant human role in shaping the biogeological environment of the planet over the last 150 years. While humans have a long history of environmental impact, it is only relatively recently, since the advent of the Industrial Revolution (ca. 1760), that the rise in our use of coal, oil, and natural gas as our dominant sources of energy has dramatically accelerated our transformative effect on Earth (Ruddiman 2005). We must contend with these changes and their impact on human health.

The field that addresses such issues is a subdomain of global health known as **environmental health**. WHO defines environmental health as encompassing all the physical, chemical, and biological factors external to a person and all the environmentally related factors that impact human behavior. Two key concepts in this domain are: (1) **environmental risk factors**, which are the specific ways environmental features and events threaten human health, and (2) **health-based environmental indicators**, which are measures designed to describe the status of human health as a result of environmental threats to health. An essential step in understanding global health is recognizing how environmental and nonenvironmental factors interact in the production of disease.

The importance of societal–environmental interaction in global health was evident, for example, in the case of the massive Gulf Oil Spill of 2010, during which about 4.9 million barrels of highly toxic crude oil poured into the ocean over the course of 152 days following an explosion on the Deepwater Horizon oil rig. Human decisions and actions, such as allowing deep water oil pumping in the first place, using less than the safest drill strategy, and the prolonged effort to cap the leaking well, combined with natural forces like ocean currents to produce the environmental and health-threatening disaster that developed.

The overall significance of environmental health (see figure 3.1) is suggested by WHO (Prüss-Üstün and Corvalán 2006), which reports:

- An estimated 24% of the global disease burden and 23% of all deaths in the world can be attributed to environmental risk factors.
- The proportion is even higher at 36% among children 0–14 years of age.
- There are notable regional differences in the environmental contribution to various diseases, with 25% of all deaths in devel-

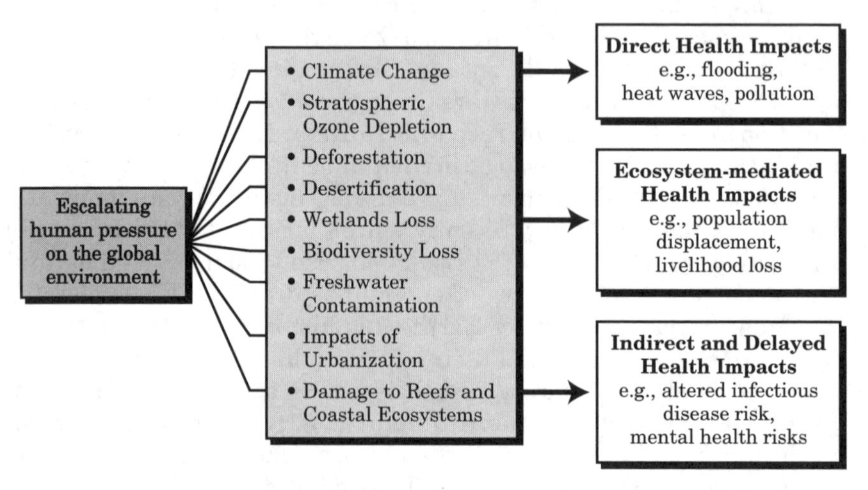

Adapted from Ecosystem and Human Well-Being: Health Synthesis, WHO 2005a.

Figure 3.1 Harmful Effects of Anthropogenic Environmental Change.

oping regions being attributable to environmental causes compared to only 17% of deaths in developed regions.

Given the contribution of environmental risk factors to the global health burden, an important part of the effort to improve global health involves the assessment, mitigation, and elimination of environmental factors that can damage health. This work includes consideration of both human impact on the environment and environmental impact on human health.

GLOBAL WARMING

Over the last 400,000 years, research indicates that the concentration of CO^2 (carbon dioxide) in Earth's atmosphere has ranged between 180 and 280 parts per million (PPM); at present, however, we are approaching 380 PPM. Other gases produced by human activity include methane, nitrous oxide, the chlorofluorocarbons, and ozone, which are also building in the atmosphere. Anthropogenic sources of atmospheric methane include rice farming, livestock production, bacterial decay in landfills and sewage, leakage during fossil fuel mining, escape from natural gas pipelines, and biomass burning (Hansen et al. 2000). The buildup of these gases in Earth's atmosphere is having a dramatic impact on the planet. Most climate scientists agree that the main cause of global warming is the human production of an atmospheric greenhouse effect that traps solar heat that otherwise would radiate back into space.

Although there has been much public debate over the last two decades about whether global warming is occurring, today there is scientific consensus that "the evidence is unequivocal; the Earth is warming and our climate is changing" (American Public Health Association 2011:6). This climatic change has grave implications for global health because even a modest increase in Earth's surface temperature tends to have a dramatic effect on life on the planet. Global warming is not a one-dimensional progression. Rather, there are diverse and sometimes extreme environmental expressions of this process, including: (1) glacial melting and ocean heating that cause oceans to rise and coastal flooding; (2) increases in the frequency and intensity of extreme weather that also cause flooding; (3) the spread of disease vectors, such as mosquitoes, flies, sand flies, lice, fleas, ticks, mites, and rodents, to new (now warmer) locations; (4) increases in wildfires; (5) jumps in the number of allergy sufferers as a result of increased allergen production; and (6) increased prevalence of asthma and other respiratory conditions. Global warming represents the most severe threat to global health in the twenty-first century and the "greatest emerging humanitarian challenge of our time" (Global Humanitarian Forum 2009:2). To put this into perspective, the last ice age involved a drop of only four or five degrees in global temperature. Current research suggests an increase of seven degrees by 2020.

Climatic change of the magnitude projected will have severe consequences for human well-being around the world. The Global Humanitarian Forum (2009), a scientific think tank established in 2007 by former UN Secretary General Kofi Annan estimates that anthropogenic climate change is already causing 300,000 deaths each year, especially from malnutrition, diarrheal diseases, and malaria, while adversely impacting the lives of as many as 300 million people around the planet. The forum estimates that by 2025, 20 million people will be forced into poverty because of the negative impacts of global warming on food production and 75 million will be displaced from their homes, many of whom will become long-term refugees, a group that tends to have poor health compared to settled populations. The United Nations Office for the Coordination of Humanitarian Affairs (2008) reports that at least 36 million people were forced to flee sudden-onset environmental disasters in 2008; of these, over 20 million were displaced by extreme weather. Many more were displaced by slower-onset climate-related disasters such as drought.

Critical sites for climate-related population displacement include the low-lying islands of the world. In Tuvalu, a nation comprised of the nine westernmost islands of Polynesia, global warming is not a future event: "Already Tuvaluans are experiencing the erosion of their beaches, damaging tidal surges [and flooding], and the intrusion of saltwater into cultivated areas" (Baer and Singer 2009:55). In the words of David Stanley (2007), "As ocean levels continue to rise, the entire population of Tuvalu may have to evacuate, third world victims of first world affluence." Concerns about the potential flooding produced by global warming are by no means limited to small low-lying islands. Major cities of the world also are at risk. With over 600 miles of densely populated coastline, the people of New York City rank among the top-ten worldwide urban populations vulnerable to coastal flooding (Rosenzweig et al. 2011). Overall, it is estimated that as much as 44 percent of the world's population lives within 150 kilometers of a coastline (United Nations Atlas of the Oceans 2010).

Based on the impact of global warming on global health described thus far, it is already evident that poor nations are experiencing the most serious health effects, and this pattern is likely to continue and increase over time. In particular, the poorest countries in Southeast Asia and southern Africa endure the greatest health impacts of global warming. One of the ironies of global warming and health is that it impacts most severely those who are the least likely to have produced greenhouse gases because they also have the fewest resources to cope with the effects of a heating planet. The consequences of global warming include both exacerbations of existing threats to health, such as further degradation of freshwater availability, a reduction in food production, and an increase in storm- and flood-related damage, as well as the emergence of new threats, such as future armed conflict over dwindling resources.

STORMS AND DISASTERS

Day after grueling day during the fall of 2005, people watched the effects of Hurricane Katrina, the worst "natural" disaster in US history. Approximately 1,600 residents of Louisiana died in Hurricane Katrina and almost 200,000 more were displaced from their homes, many never to return. According to analyses carried out by Patrick Sharkey (2007) of Harvard University, old age (65 and older) was the single most important factor in determining who fell victim to the storm and the floodwaters it unleashed. The death rate for the elderly population in the city was more than 15 times as high as that for younger people. Yet, age itself was not the only issue.

In the 2000 census, about 19 percent of the white population in New Orleans was 65 or older, compared to just 9 percent of the black population. Yet, African Americans constituted 58 percent of elderly individuals who died in Katrina compared to 38 percent among whites. Among those under 65 years of age who were killed in Katrina, 82 percent were African American compared to 17 percent among whites. Affirming the importance of place, neighborhood tracts with relatively high death counts had, on average, relatively high proportions of African American residents and relatively few white residents. For example, the average land tract with zero deaths was 56 percent black and 40 percent white, whereas the average tract with 10 or more deaths was 78 percent black and 20 percent white. Further, compared to whites, African Americans were less likely to be evacuated before the storm and four times more likely to lose their jobs after the storm. Not surprisingly, they also reported higher levels of postdisaster stress (Elliott and Pais 2006). As these data suggest, *social inequality*, reflected in ethnicity and class, had a major influence on the effects of Hurricane Katrina. Such inequalities are common in disasters.

Research shows that men and women are not affected in the same ways by disasters like Hurricane Katrina. They have different exposure to risk; level of preparedness; extent of physical, psychological, socioeconomic impacts; emergency response; and postdisaster recovery (Neumayer and Plümper 2007). For example, disasters are known to lead to increased levels of domestic violence against women and higher levels of posttraumatic stress disorder. In the case of Hurricane Katrina, the rate of gender-based violence (including both sexual assault and domestic violence) in Mississippi rose from 4.6 per 100,000 per day before the hurricane to 16.3 per 100,000 per day a year later, a period during which many women were displaced from their homes and were living in temporary shelters (Anastario et al. 2009).

In a time of global warming, Hurricane Katrina is neither a unique nor an isolated climatic event. NASA scientists at the Goddard Institute for Space Studies have developed climate simulation models that indicate severe storms and hurricanes may become more common as Earth's climate warms. The NASA models predict severe thunderstorms will produce damaging winds on the ground, wreaking havoc in urban areas in particular. Moreover, there is growing scientific evidence that global warming enhances hurricane strength, threatening coastal areas and the people who live in hurricane zones with massive flooding and storm surges. Several recent computer simulation models (e.g., Bender et al. 2010) suggest a doubling of the frequency of category four and five storms[1] by the end of the twenty-first century. Another study by Young and coworkers (2011) describes a global trend of increasing ocean wind speed and wave height over the last quarter century.

Because of tragic events like Hurricane Katrina it is clear that, while hurricanes are natural hazards—"acts of god" in the nonreligious legal sense—they can begin as a result of anthropogenic changes in the environment and quickly develop into **unnatural disasters**. In such unnatural disasters the level of suffering, death, and destruction is exacerbated by human acts of commission and omission that may be intentional or unintentional. As Katrina demonstrated, unnatural disasters produce a social distribution of adverse health impacts that reflects the preexisting social structures of inequality in access to critical life resources.

The 2010 earthquake that devastated Haiti, a country with one of the worst health profiles in the world, is another example of a disastrous event. In Haiti, the infant mortality rate[2] (a common public health indicator of the level of health in a country) is 54.02 per 1,000 live births compared to an overall world rate of 41.61 and a US rate of 6.06 (WHO 2011c). The devastating 7.0 quake that struck on January 12, 2010, killed as many as 300,000 people, including some 300 health workers. It injured countless more, left a million-and-a-half people homeless, and further damaged the already threadbare infrastructure of the country (Daniell 2011). Yet, it is fair to say that this was not a natural disaster. As Peter Hallward, Kingston University professor and author of the book *Damming the Flood: Haiti, Aristide, and the Politics of Containment*, critically observes in his *Guardian* article:

> Any large city in the world would have suffered extensive damage from an earthquake on the scale of the one that ravaged Haiti's capital city . . ., but it's no accident that so much of Port-au-Prince now looks like a war zone. Much of the devastation wreaked by this latest and most calamitous disaster to befall Haiti is best understood as another thoroughly manmade outcome of a long and ugly historical sequence . . . the result of [a] . . . history of deliberate impoverishment and disempowerment. Haiti is routinely described as the "poorest country in the western hemisphere." This poverty is the direct legacy of perhaps the most brutal system of colonial exploitation in world history, compounded by decades of systematic postcolonial oppression. (Hallward 2010)

Further complicating Haiti's grave health crisis, in the aftermath of the earthquake an epidemic of cholera began north of the capital and spread throughout the whole country. By July 2012, almost 600,000 cholera cases had been identified and almost 7,500 people had died of the disease (Pan American Health Organization 2011).

As Hurricane Katrina and the Haitian earthquake indicate, health and disease are always shaped by the historic structures of social relationships and their material products.

CASE STUDY
The Inuit and Climate Change

Stark as it is, the projected death toll from global climate change does not tell the whole story of the health-impacting transformations that are underway. An important health-related aspect of climate change is the lived-experience of the people most intensely affected. One expression of this experience is seen among Inuit peoples of Alaska and Canada. The term *Inuit* describes the indigenous hunting, trapping, and fishing people who have inhabited the Arctic environment for thousands of years.

Assessment of climate change in the Arctic is prompted by the fact that many environmental effects of planetary warming are seen and expected to be most intense in this region. For a number of years Inuit have reported emergent anthropogenic climate-related perils to their way of life, including adverse impacts on land travel, hunting, fishing, and other basic subsistence activities. According to an indigenous leader, "Arctic . . . peoples are threatened with the extinction or catastrophic decline of entire bird, fish and wildlife populations, including species of caribou, seals and fish critical to . . . food security" (quoted in Bodley 2008:221).

As part of a National Geographic initiative (Bowermaster 2007), climate change educators traveled 1,000 miles through the Arctic, stopping at each Inuit settlement along the way and engaging community members in conversation about their experience of climate change. People talked about fast-melting ice causing unexpected decreases in hunting days and greater difficulty constructing ice-block igloos with lower than usual amounts of snow and ice. These changes are without precedent in Inuit memory. Three experienced Inuit hunters traveled with the team and pointed out clear physical evidence of the effects of climate change, such as the way shifting winds were reshaping ice formations used for generations as critical landmarks in difficult terrain. Consequences of these changes included hunters falling through melted ice, homes slipping from the melting tundra into the ocean, and people switching from a diet high in wild-caught protein to one based on less-nutritious, store-bought processed food. According to Barry Smit, a researcher at the University of Guelph in Canada, "The stores only have food that's easy to transport and doesn't perish, so there are no vegetables. The young people are increasingly eating highly processed junk food, so we are seeing more teeth problems and obesity" (quoted in Davies 2010).

Another potential impact involves Inuit mental health. Glenn Albrecht of the University of Newcastle in Australia has introduced the psychological concept of **solastalgia** to draw attention to the importance of environmentally induced distress among those whose habitat is changing around them (Albrecht et al. 2007). While nostalgia refers to the homesickness people may feel when away from home (e.g., among refugees), solastalgia labels the emotional upset produced by environmental disruption that befalls people while they are in their home setting. Evidence of solastalgia has been found by Albrecht and coworkers among people who have been subject to climate change–related experiences of persistent drought and among people living near open-cut coal mining in New South Wales, Australia. In both cases, people experienced a sense of powerlessness or lack of control over the changes going on around them.

These findings are supported by the analyses being done by cultural geographers and anthropologists on the importance of a "sense of place" in human identity and well-being (Feld and Basso 1996). While research on solastalgia has not yet been conducted among Inuit, the psychological impact of climate change among them and other social groups subject to ecosystem degradation (like the Tuvalu Islanders discussed in this chapter and the Appalachian miners in chapter 2) is an emergent issue in global health. Notably in this regard, in March 2007, Inuit representative and Nobel Prize nominee Sheilah Watt-Cloutier, accompanied by 60 Inuit hunters, filed a petition with the Inter-American Commission on Human Rights. The petition charged the United States, as one of the largest producers of greenhouse gases, with violating Inuit human rights under the American Declaration on the Rights and Duties of Man and the American Convention on Human Rights (Cherrington 2008).

This action reflects one of the ways people have actively responded to the adverse impacts of climate change. Other kinds of response are also unfolding. Based on a study of Sach's Harbour, an

Inuit community in Canada's Western Arctic, Fikret Berkes and Dyanna Jolly (2001) concluded that local ability to cope successfully with and adjust to the health and social challenges of climate change will be determined by people's **resilience**, including acceptance of a flexible seasonal hunting pattern, commitment to passing down across generations detailed traditional knowledge about the environment, and maintenance of inter- and intracommunity-sharing relationships in harsh times. While these initial insights are useful, "we are still very far from recognizing the full extent of culturally diverse responses to environmental degradation and climate change at local and national levels around the world. . . . Ethnographic research and anthropological theory are both very much needed to close this gap" (Baer and Thomas 2011:2).

THREATS TO THE AIR WE BREATHE

Global warming is not the only anthropogenic environmental risk facing humankind. The list of the kinds of environmental degradations wrought by humans is disturbingly long, including deforestation, toxic ocean-dumping, land salinization and desertification, species extinction, acid rain, buildup of plastic waste on land and in the ocean, and air pollution. The last of these, air pollution, is of special note because of the significant immediate health threats it presents. Air pollution is defined as an atmospheric condition in which various substances are present at concentrations high enough above their normal ambient levels to produce a measurable adverse effect on people, animals, and vegetation.

Consciousness about air pollution was first raised when London was hit by the "killer fog." On the morning of December 5, 1952, Londoners woke to find their city heavily blanketed by a toxic and stagnant mix of impenetrable fog and sooty, black, coal smoke that stayed four days before winds finally cleared the air. The source was the thick sulfurous output of local factories and over a million coal-burning stoves in the London basin. It is estimated that sulfur dioxide levels in London during December 1952 reached 700 parts per billion (PPB), several times greater than normal. Particulate matter concentrations in the air are estimated to have ranged between 3,000 and 14,000 micrograms, with the highest levels being 50 times greater than normal (Singer 2010). While many health and political authorities did not fully appreciate the magnitude of the cataclysm, undertakers and florists knew there was a problem: they ran out of caskets and flowers.

Investigation by the British Ministry of Health concluded that during the first three weeks of December the deadly fog caused 3,000 excess mortalities in London—three times higher than expected for that time of year. A reanalysis of hospital, insurance, and other records by Michelle Bell and Devra Davis (2001:393) concluded that: "The true scope and scale of the health effects linked with London's lethal smog extended over a longer period than originally estimated . . . [with] unusually high mortality rates [of approximately 12,000] for a period of 2.5 months," affirming the very deadly nature of this air pollution event. Since the killer fog, changes in policies and practices in London facilitated successful abatement of the specific pollutants that produced the disaster.

Anthropogenic air pollution, however, has reemerged as a significant global health problem. WHO (2002) reports that 900,000 people die each year from causes directly attributable to outdoor air pollution. Within a developed nation like the United States, which is a major producer of air pollution, it is estimated that as many as half a million people die annually from cardiopulmonary disease linked to breathing particulate matter (fine particle) pollution (found in smoke and haze) circulating in the air. Air pollution has also become acute in the densely populated megacities of the developing world. Dhaka, the capital of Bangladesh; Mumbai, India; and Mexico City exemplify this growing global health problem. According to a report from the Department of Environment of Bangladesh, in 2006–2007 the density of airborne particulate matter in Dhaka reached the highest particulate-matter level in the world.

In Bangladesh, respiratory problems now comprise one of the top causes of mortality and morbidity, while the share of the total burden of disease attributable to respiratory infections and disease is about one-third higher than the average for other Southeast Asian countries (WHO 2002). In Dhaka, respiratory problems are the annual source of an estimated 15,000 premature deaths, as well as several million cases of pulmonary, lung, and even neurological diseases (World Bank 2006). Research in Bangladesh (Hassan et al. 2002) shows that seven million people in the country have asthma; most of them children, who breathe in more air relative to lung size than adults and spend more time outdoors during periods of the day when pollution levels are highest. Asthma in children was significantly higher in low-income households and households with low literacy levels. Exacerbating the lived-experience of asthma sufferers in Bangladesh is the common belief that the disease is contagious, leading to the social isolation of affected individuals. Other childhood diseases caused or worsened by air pollution, including bronchitis and chronic cough, have also skyrocketed in Bangladesh in recent years.

In Dhaka, old and poorly serviced vehicles, brick kilns, dust from roads and construction sites, and toxic fumes from industrial sites (e.g., garment manufacturing plants, tanneries, paper mills, and vehicle and appliance assembly plants) comprise the major sources of air pollution. Tanneries in particular emit an array of dangerous toxic gasses, including hydrogen sulfide, ammonia, and chlorine into the environment (Bangladesh Department of the Environment 2002).

Worldwide, motor vehicles are a significant source of air pollution. They have become a highly desired modern marker of personal success, contributing to an ever-greater number of vehicles on the roads. Today, motor vehicles are concentrated in the developed countries, but as nations develop, so does their appetite for motor vehicles. China and India account for about 36 percent of the world's population, but at present have less than 47 vehicles per 1,000 people compared to the industrialized countries with 500–800 vehicles per 1,000 people. The impact of rising numbers of vehicles in these two rapidly developing countries alone could be devastating to global health. Researchers in the United Kingdom found a strong correlation between pneumonia-related deaths and air pollution from motor vehicles (Knox 2008). Cities around the world with high exposure to air pollutants from motor vehicles, industrial production, and other causes face mounting rates of asthma, pneumonia, and other lower respiratory infections among children. Even in areas of the world with limited air pollution, public health consequences can be high because negative health effects can occur even at low levels of some airborne chemicals. Overall, the poor, who are more likely to live in more highly polluted areas because housing is more affordable there, experience the greatest harm from rising levels of air pollution. Studies in Sao Paulo, Brazil, and Hamilton, Canada (Jerrett et al. 2004; Martins et al. 2004), for example, show greater levels of risk for respiratory diseases in areas with predominantly poor populations.

These findings on air pollution raise the issue of **environmental justice**. This concept emerged in response to growing recognition of the unequal sociogeographic distribution of environmental hazards and industrial hazardous waste. A related term, **environmental racism**, refers to the enactment or enforcement of any policy, practice, or regulation that negatively affects the living environment of low-income and/or ethnically marginalized communities at a higher rate than affluent communities (Checker 2005, 2008). For example, the Commission for Racial Justice (1987) found that three of the five largest waste facilities dealing with hazardous materials in the United States were located in poor African American communities. Similarly, a study of government data initiated by the Associated Press found that African Americans are 79 percent more likely than whites to live in neighborhoods where industrial pollution is suspected of causing the greatest health dangers (Pace 2005). This is not just a problem of urban areas; it is common in rural settings as well (Singer 2011a).

POISONS AROUND US

Toxic chemicals, both naturally occurring and man-made, often get into the human body. We may inhale them, swallow them in contaminated food or water, or absorb them through the skin. There are even cultural practices that introduce toxins into the body, be they the use of mercury in dentistry or lead in a few folk medicines and traditional ceramic glazes. Immediate exposure to toxins is not the only risk; people working in or otherwise visiting contaminated areas can bring toxins (e.g., pesticides) home on their clothing. Toxic substances like lead, arsenic, cadmium, 2-butoxyethanol, and beryllium are ingredients in many common household products (e.g., cosmetics, cleaning products).

The global chemical industry regularly introduces new chemicals on the market. The Natural Resources Defense Council, an environmental protection group, reported that most of the 84,000 chemicals that are registered in the United States for commercial use have never been fully assessed for their potential toxic effects on human health (Chilkov 2010). Many of these chemicals reach the most vulnerable—fetuses and newborns. A study of over 250 pregnant women in the United States found that almost all had detectable levels of eight categories of chemicals in their blood or urine, including pesticides, flame retardants, PFCs (perfluorinated chemicals) used in nonstick cookware and Gore-Tex, phthalates (found in many fragrances and plastics), pollution from car exhaust, perchlorate (found in rocket fuel), and PCBs (polychlorinated biphenyl, which were banned in 1979 but still persist in the environment) (Szabo 2011). Over 350 anthropogenic contaminants have been found in human breast milk, including over 80 dioxin or dioxin-like chemicals and almost 200 volatile compounds. In children, the developmental impacts of dioxins and PCBs include decreases in physical stamina, reduced eye–hand coordination, memory loss, and diminished cognitive ability (World Wildlife Federation-UK 1999).

Some chemicals that enter the body are broken down into other substances, called metabolites, and may remain in the body for only a short period of time. Arsenic, for example, is mostly excreted within 72 hours of exposure. Others, like lead, persist longer and cause harm over a period of time. **Body burden** is a term used to refer both to the burden of a specific toxin and to the total amount of toxic substances present in a human body at a given point in time. **Biomonitoring** is the measurement of the body burden of toxic chemicals.

Environmental Defense, an activist organization, did a biomonitoring study of toxic chemicals in the bodies of people living across Canada. One participant, Sarah Winterton, found that her body was home to 16 respiratory toxins, 38 reproductive toxins, 19 chemicals

Community rubbish dump, Funafuti Atoll, Tuvalu. (Julie Park)

that disrupt hormones, and 27 carcinogens (White 2006). The study also found traces of heavy metals, such as lead; arsenic and uranium; and chemicals used in pesticides, flame retardants, and stain repellents in her body. Similar studies of volunteers in Europe and the United States have also found multiple chemicals in many people. Some researchers suspect these toxic chemicals are linked to a number of cancers, including breast, testicular, and non-Hodgkin's lymphoma, as well as reproductive disorders, learning disabilities, and other diseases, although this continues to be an area of uncertainty and debate.

Among these top pollutant threats to human health is lead, an indestructible heavy metal that can accumulate in the body. Lead has been called "the mother of all industrial poisons . . . the paradigmatic toxin [linking] industrial and environmental disease" (Markowitz and Rosner 2002:137). In use in human communities for over 5,000 years, lead levels in inhabited environments began to increase dramatically with the Industrial Revolution. Children are at greatest risk for lead poisoning for three primary reasons: (1) they do not consume enough food to slow absorption; (2) they absorb as much as 50 percent of inhaled lead, significantly more than adults, and tend to spend more time close to the ground or floor where lead dust accumulates; and (3) their rapidly developing nervous systems are highly sensitive to lead's toxic effects.

The consequences of lead exposure include disruption of biological systems involving the alteration of three processes: molecular interactions, intercell signaling, and cell functioning. Thus, lead poisoning has long been linked to a range of health problems, including nervous system damage, decreased IQ, stunted growth, sterility, hyperactivity, impaired hearing, seizures, and death. Globally, this primarily anthropogenic environmental threat is of special importance in developing nations where multiple sites of intensive lead exposure in children have been identified: Tianjin, China; La Oroya, Peru; Dzerzhinsk, Russia; and Kabwe, Zambia (Blacksmith Institute 2007). For example, Kabwe, the second largest city in Zambia, was once a prosperous lead and zinc mining community, where lead was smelted for almost a century until 1994. Although now closed, the mine left a dark legacy in Kabwe. While "safe blood levels" (many contend there is no safe level for lead) are said to be less than 10 micrograms per deciliter (mcg/dl) of blood, disturbing levels higher than 200 mcg/dl have been recorded in children in Kabwe. Children who play in the soil and young men who scavenge the defunct mine area for leftover bits of salable metal are most at risk.

Overall, it is estimated that 120 million people around the world are currently overexposed to lead—three times the number infected by HIV/AIDS (*The Hindu* 2012). Francesca Valent and collaborators (2004) point out that exposure to lead and its health consequences are most common among socially disadvantaged groups because the poor are far more likely to live in substandard and more hazardous housing, to suffer from nutrient-deficient diets, to have greater exposure to stressors, and to be exposed to harmful living and working conditions.

Illustrative of the risk lead poses for poor communities, in the spring of 2010, Médecins Sans Frontières (Doctors Without Borders) encountered an epidemic of lead poisoning in several northern Nigerian villages when they arrived during the country's annual immunization program. Men from the impacted villages, most of whom were poor and illiterate, carried rock containing gold ore home from several small mining operations. Unbeknownst to the men, the ore also contained very high lead levels. Consequently, when the rock was crushed to extract the gold, lead dust blew all around. The scope of the lead contamination was unprecedented—at least 160, and possibly as many as 400 died, with hundreds of people suffering lead poisoning, especially children. People in the villages who were unaware of lead toxicity attributed the deaths and sickness to malaria. In the assessment of Joseph Amon (2010), director of health and human rights at Human Rights Watch, "The tragedy unfolding in Zamfara is not a simple act of nature. Rather, it's the latest testament to the Nigerian government's failure to make the health of its citizens a priority." Despite significant oil wealth, Nigeria's medical and public health systems are underfunded and ineffective. According to Andrew McCartor and his colleagues at the Blacksmith Institute, "This tragedy should serve as a reminder to us all that toxic pollution is not an abstract problem for future generations, but an acute challenge that impacts millions of lives today" (2010:5).

Beyond lead, numerous additional toxins are regularly released into the environment and cause immense harm to humans. The global health impacts from toxic pollutants such as heavy metals, pesticides, and radionuclides are greater than previously thought. Today, it is estimated that more than 100 million people are at risk from toxic pollution at levels above international health standards. This is a public health issue as salient as tuberculosis, malaria, and HIV/AIDS—and is one that should receive considerably more attention and resources (McCartor et al. 2010).

PLURALEA AND THE HUMAN HEALTH FUTURE

One shortcoming of separately discussing global warming and other expressions of anthropogenic environmental degradation is that *there are significant interactions that occur among and worsen the impact of individual environmental crises.* The term **pluralea** (meaning multiple threats) has been suggested within anthropology to label this kind of synergy in which the health damage produced is greater than merely adding up the health consequences of two or more copresent environmental threats (Singer 2009a, 2010). Pluralea interactions can negatively impact air, land, and water environments on which human populations depend for survival.

An example of a potential case of pluralea interaction involves air quality and occurs because pollution usually is a complex mixture of toxins. A review of existing laboratory-based experimental studies involving both animals and humans by Mauderly and Samet (2009), identified measurable adverse synergisms between ozone (O^3) and various other air pollutants.[3] In experimental research, bodily functions of individuals exposed to O^3 and other air pollutants in combination were compromised (e.g., in terms of heart rate, breathing pattern, lung volume, forced exhalation) more than the sum total of negative effects produced by each individual pollutant exposure. In an even more complex pluralea interaction, global climate change is likely contributing to the impact of O^3 levels in several ways: by causing higher temperatures, increasing local humidity, multiplying greater biogenic volatile organic compound emissions, and producing more frequent wildfires that release additional pollutants, including particulate matter, into the air (Millstein and Harley 2009).

Measurable health consequences of such interactions are beginning to be documented. Research in Wuhan, China, known as "oven city" because of its high summer temperatures, found synergistic effects between elevated temperatures and particulate matter in the air (PM_{10}) that increased daily cardiovascular and cardiopulmonary mortality in the city (Qian et al. 2008). Epidemiological evidence from other Chinese cities also indicates significant risks of ozone interactions with increasing temperatures produced by global warming (Zhang et al. 2006).

Research on diesel fuel shows that it plays a unique role in respiratory mortality caused by diesel-generated particulate matter, which is small enough to pass deep into human lungs and carries anthropogenic carcinogenic compounds pulled from the atmosphere (Pope 2000). Moreover, the combustion of diesel fuel is a significant source of greenhouse gas production, creating 25 to 400 times the amount of particulate black carbon (a product of incomplete combustion of fossil and other fuels) and organic matter as the combustion of regular gasoline (Jacobson 2008). Global warming, in turn, magnifies the toxicity of these and other air pollutants. Noyes and associates note that "climate change coupled with air pollutant exposures may have potentially serious adverse consequences for human health in urban and [other] polluted regions" (2009:971).

Pluralea interactions occur on land as well. Thus, the United Nations Millennium Ecosystem Assessment (2007), which ranks land degradation among the world's gravest environmental challenges, reports that 40 percent of the world's agricultural land has been seriously degraded by the combined and interacting effects of poor farming practices, deforestation, and climate change. One expression of this was witnessed in 2008 when stable food prices soared and millions of people around the world faced the threat of hunger and starvation, resulting in angry antigovernment street demonstrations in many countries from Egypt to Haiti and from Cameroon to Bangladesh. What caused the surge in the cost of food? An assessment by the United Nations Environment Programme concluded that the "combined effects" of land degradation as a result of overusage, dwindling water tables, climate change, and invasive species were to blame (Nellemann et al. 2009). All of these problems are anthropogenic and almost all are interactive.

The problem continues to grow. On March 11, 2011, Ban Ki-moon, the Secretary-General of the United Nations, told the UN General Assembly (UN News Centre 2011):

> Global food prices have [again] reached record levels, and LDCs [Lesser Developed Countries] face a real prospect of a new food cri-

> sis. Millions of people have been pushed into poverty by the latest food price rises. . . . When prices go up, they go hungry. Women and children are the worst hit.

Global health is also threatened by pluralea interactions in the oceans, lakes, and Earth's other hydraulic systems. The interactive pluralea processes of overfishing and global warming are having a notable impact in marine environments (Singer 2010). Because of overfishing and global warming, we are approaching a world 40 years from now of rising seas empty of fish and devoid of ice (Feldman 2008). Similarly, the United Nations Environmental Programme warns of the food availability impacts of the merging of climate change, water pollution, overharvesting of fishing stocks, and invasive species infestations in the world's fishing zones (Nellemann et al. 2008).

Not surprisingly, the impact of pluralea processes is not evenly distributed across social groups. Some groups, most notably the people of poor countries and the poor and disadvantaged of all countries, disproportionately suffer the cumulative effects of multiple ecocrises as well as the further burden of ecocrises interactions.

INFECTIOUS DISEASES, CHRONIC DISEASES, AND MENTAL HEALTH

Biomedicine traditionally has differentiated *acute* from *chronic* diseases; *infectious* from *noninfectious* diseases; and diseases of the *body* from diseases of the *mind*. While these differentiations may be heuristically useful in guiding medical responses, global health research shows that in many instances they do not reflect objective realities. Rather, they are biomedical cultural constructions based on prevailing conventions about the nature of disease.

Diseases like cancer, which were formerly thought of as chronic, noncommunicable threats to health, have been shown in a number of cases to have an infectious origin. Examples include the role of the pathogen *Helicobacter pylori* in the development of gastric adenocarcinoma and peptic ulcer disease, the part played by the human papilloma virus in the onset of cervical cancer, and the contribution of human herpes virus 8 to the development of the skin cancer Kaposi's sarcoma. Additionally, after suffering some infectious diseases, patients are at risk for chronic sequalae (i.e., a chronic condition resulting from an acute condition), for example, maternal infections during pregnancy, even without directly infecting the child, can increase the child's risk for chronic neurological and pulmonary diseases or chickenpox.

Some diseases, such as AIDS, were conceived of as acutely threatening conditions that, without the development of a cure, would cause premature death. With the development and dissemination of treatments, however, these diseases have become chronic conditions with long-term prognoses. Another complication involves the ways that the initial stages of an acute infection can cause later-in-life chronic disabilities, such as the role of poliovirus in late-onset neurological deterioration.

Finally, separation of the mind and body in disease has proven to be particularly problematic in cases where diseases of the body cause mental health problems. Herpes simplex virus type 2 can cause schizophrenia; the presence of diabetes significantly increases the odds of comorbid depression. Mental and emotional factors also have an effect on physical well-being—stress can lead to cardiovascular disease.

These caveats notwithstanding, a useful and revealing starting point when exploring global health considers the global scope, distribution, health burden, and public health responses to some of the major infectious, chronic, and mental health diseases of the world.

Infectious Diseases

A critically important trait of infectious diseases is that they are spread from one person to another, or from an animal to a person or vice versa. Infectious diseases are transmitted through contact with infectious agents like bacteria, viruses, parasites, prions, fungi, and protozoa. Transmission can be direct, such as through breathing in the water droplets exhaled by another, or indirect, such as touching something touched by an infected individual. The spread of some infectious disease agents requires a vector like the different species of mosquito that spread West Nile virus, malaria, and dengue. Still common in many parts of the world is the mistaken belief that HIV can be spread by a mosquito rather than through direct contact with an infected person's body fluids, a transfusion with infected blood, an accidental needle stick, or mother-to-child transmission by birth or breastfeeding (currently a rare occurrence).

Without doubt, infectious diseases have profoundly affected human history, life experience, and biology. Some, infectious diseases, like the plague and the flu, have devastated human populations in ancient and modern times. Those that contribute to infant mortality have probably claimed more lives than all the wars in human history, all noninfectious diseases, and all natural/unnatural disasters combined. Over 9.5 million people die each year due to infectious diseases—the vast majority of these people live in developing countries. Overall, infectious diseases account for about 35 percent of the total mortality and 40 percent of the number of life-years lost because of sickness, disability, and death in low- and middle-income communities

(Black et al. 2003). More broadly, as anthropologists Ann Herring and Alan Swedlund indicate, as a result of the emergence in recent years of new, rapidly or widely spreading infectious diseases like HIV/AIDS, SARS, and various influenzas,

> we live in a time obsessed with killer germs. . . . People worldwide feel a growing sense of vulnerability and uncertainty with respect to infectious diseases [and the] expanding list of pathogens—referred to as "emerging infections." As knowledge about pathogens is . . . disseminated through various media to enter public consciousness . . . , anxiety is rekindled about mortality on the scale of historic plagues such as the fourteenth-century Black Death in Europe. (2010:1)

Remarkably, since the mid-1970s, previously unknown infectious diseases have been discovered at the rapid pace of one per year and most involve newly identified viruses. Global warming contributes to the global spread of old and new infectious diseases, in part because human disease vectors previously restricted in their distribution by seasonal temperatures have begun invading new areas in response to climate changes. This applies to water-borne infectious agents as well. A temperature rise of only 2°C would more than double the metabolism rate of mosquitoes, including species that spread deadly human diseases such as malaria. Global warming at this level could also expand malaria's domain of active infection from its current 42 percent to 60 percent of the planet. Vector-borne ailments currently being spread by global warming include malaria, West Nile virus, Rift Valley Fever, Yellow Fever, Lyme disease, plague, and dengue.

Beyond global warming, other environmental changes contribute to infectious disease outbreaks around the world. Socio-ecological transformations in farming regions, such as agricultural intensification, contribute to the spread of infections as human populations move into new habitats. Similarly, the growth in the size and number of megacities, with populations over 10 million, and the tendency for large numbers of poor people to be concentrated in densely populated urban areas with comparatively few health and social services, also facilitate the rapid spread of infectious diseases.

From AIDS to Zygomyosis (a fungal disease), there is a long list of infectious diseases that affect humans. The impact of any particular infectious disease varies across a number of dimensions:

- Region of the world—e.g., although a global disease, HIV/AIDS is of far greater importance in sub-Saharan African than Central America.
- Economic status—e.g., helminth infections (worms) are particularly impactful in poor countries, although overall infections of many types are more common and more damaging to health

among the poor because of living and working conditions and less access to medical and public health resources.

- Gender—e.g., tuberculosis tends to affect males more than females.
- Age—e.g., infectious diarrheal diseases have the most impact on small children.

CASE STUDY
Dengue

Dengue is possibly the world's most rapidly increasing vector-borne disease, with over 2.5 billion people in over 100 countries at risk. Every year 50–100 million people are newly infected (WHO 2004a). The spread of dengue, and the increasing frequency and severity of dengue epidemics, is driven by rapid and uncontrolled urbanization, social inequity, and the tenacity of the dengue virus and its principle mosquito vector, *Aedes aeqypti*. Dengue has been called "breakbone fever"; symptoms include stomach pain, headaches, nausea and vomiting, and pain behind the eyes.

There are four different viral strains of dengue, and coinfection with more than one strain can produce a significantly more severe and increasingly more common condition known as dengue hemorrhagic fever (DHF); each year there are approximately a quarter to a half million cases of DHF, of whom about 25,000 die (WHO 2004). During the first nine months of 2007, over 625,000 cases of dengue were reported in Latin American countries, especially Brazil, Venezuela, and Colombia, including over 12,000 cases of DHF (San Martin et al. 2010). In Mexico, there has been an alarming increase in the number of cases of DHF, which now account for approximately one quarter of dengue cases. The number of deaths due to dengue in Latin America was over 1,000 during 2010. Dengue is moving slowly into North America. Although dengue appears to be an equal-opportunity infection, affecting rich and poor alike, as anthropologist Arachu Castro observes, "dengue may spare no one, but its consequences highlight and reinforce existing social inequalities" (2010:248).

Chronic Diseases

While infectious diseases have long been a grave threat in poor, developing countries, the growing prevalence of chronic noninfectious diseases like heart disease, diabetes, and cancer now accounts for the largest burden on public health everywhere except parts of sub-Saharan Africa. This dramatic **health transition**, which results in a growing **dual health burden** (infectious and noninfectious chronic diseases) in developing countries, is being driven by several interrelated factors: (1) people worldwide are living longer; (2) they are eating unbalanced, high sugar/carbohydrate Western diets; (3) they are developing sedentary and stressful life patterns as part of the transition from rural to urban residence; and (4) they are living in industrially polluted environments with contaminated land, water, and air. These factors, when combined with the comparatively limited availability of health resources that often results in late detection and treatment, cause global health professionals to predict that the impact of noncommunicable disease in developing countries will be greater than its impact in developed countries. While the health profiles of high-income and middle- and low-income countries remain distinct, currently the differences (see figure 3.2) are not as great as they were in the past.

The increasing importance of chronic disease in developing countries can be seen in Bangladesh, discussed earlier regarding air pollution and health. Chronic diseases now account for the largest share of premature deaths and disabilities in Bangladesh, with the most common chronic conditions being heart disease and diabetes (*Chronic Disease News* 2009). The leading cause of death in the country is ischemic heart disease, which involves insufficient blood supply reaching the heart due to the thickening of artery walls as a result of the accumulation of fatty material like cholesterol. This heart condition is the cause of just over 10 percent of mortality in Bangladesh. Another important heart-related condition is cerebrovascular disease (stroke), which is the sixth leading cause of death in Bangladesh. Together, cardiovascular diseases accounted for one-fourth of all mortality in Bangladesh in

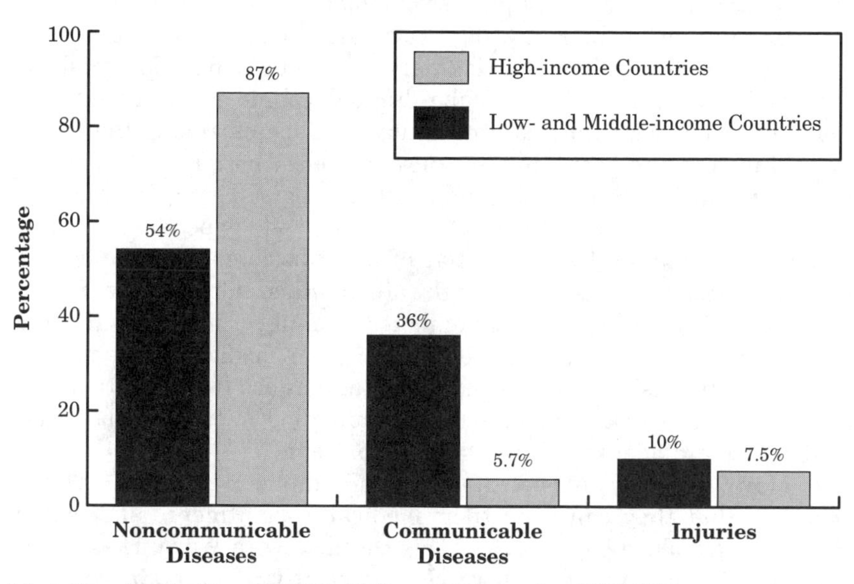

Adapted from Healthy Lives: Global Health News and Commentary, WHO 2011.

Figure 3.2 Causes of Death for High vs. Low/Middle Income Countries.

2002, causing more than a quarter of a million deaths. Another prevalent chronic disease is diabetes, the rates of which are higher in urban than in rural areas, but which in recent years has begun to be diagnosed among tribal populations in rural areas. In both urban and rural settings and across all age groups, Bangladeshi women have a higher prevalence of diabetes than men. High cholesterol and high blood pressure are commonly comorbid with diabetes in Bangladesh and elsewhere.

A typical case is that of Shilpi, a 25-year-old newlywed and teacher at a middle school in Dhaka, the capital of Bangladesh. When Shilpi was diagnosed with diabetes, she was startled as she thought of it as a disease of old people. Fearing judgment, and not wanting to be treated differently by friends and relatives because she had a major chronic disease, Shilpi began avoiding social gatherings. She also had a hard time concentrating at work after word of her condition leaked and she became the subject of gossip. Notably, as this account (reported in *Chronic Disease News* 2009) suggests, Shilpi was particularly troubled by the social consequences of her diagnosis, illustrating the **biosocial** nature of disease. The social stress she experienced could negatively impact her diabetes—not an uncommon occurrence because diseases always carry more than narrow biomedical health meanings. They may also convey cultural understandings about the character of the sufferer, the nature of his or her social group, the will of supernatural beings, and much more. There are biological consequences of social experiences and social consequences of biological experiences.

In addition to their growing prevalence in developing countries, chronic diseases are disproportionately common among impoverished, marginalized, and otherwise subordinated ethnic minority populations in developed countries. In a study of diabetes among the traditional hunting and gathering (but now settled) Aboriginal Warlpiri of the Northern Territory, Australia, anthropologist Françoise Dussart (2010) reports that diabetes is now endemic. Life expectancy for the Warlpiri is 20 years less than that of non-Aboriginal populations in the area, mostly because of the high rate at which they suffer noncommunicable chronic diseases like diabetes. Complicating things, health care providers tend to see diabetes in narrow, medical terms and to interpret patients' behavior (e.g., lack of adherence to medication and diet) as a defect in their character. This has led to tensions between health care providers and their diabetic patients.

Many providers expect their Warlpiri diabetic patients to limit travel so that they can keep their medical appointments and better manage their blood sugar levels. This conflicts with Warlpiri expectations of being free to move about visiting relatives and maintaining a culturally meaningful pattern of life. Diabetes sufferers also evade strict adherence to medical recommendations about dietary practices, weight management, and physical exercise in order to fulfill their social identities as Warlpiri. As a result of their history of colonial subordination and Australian social welfare practices (e.g., distribution or processed foods), the Warlpiri are accustomed to eating white flour, processed sugar, and tea and see these items as "proper foods" that reinforce their identity as Warlpiri. From the Warlpiri point of view, physicians are encouraging their diabetic patients to eat "improper diets" (e.g., less processed food, less sugar, more fruits and vegetables, etc.). Because food habits are among the most tenacious customs, culture trumps medical recommendation (Saethre 2011).

Mental Health

About 15 percent of the global burden of disease is attributed to mental disorders (Üstün 1999). Although the WHO (2005b) declared that there can be "no health without mental health," mental health has not been a central concern of efforts to improve global health until recently. WHO estimates that about one-third of person-years lost to disability in the world is the consequence of mental health diseases, especially unipolar depression, alcohol dependence, schizophrenia, bipolar depression, and dementia. Moreover, mental disorders are believed to account for at least one to two million deaths every year and 14 percent of all years-of-life lost. Mental disorders are intimately linked with other threats to health, such as heart disease, diabetes, HIV infection, poor maternal and child health, and injuries and accidents. Because of the enormity of the problem and the recent recognition that mental health conditions impair the ability of people to cope with and adapt to life circumstances, there is now a growing movement to promote mental health as a global health priority because:

- Mental disorders affect people in all societies, but they disproportionately impact the poor and those who are disadvantaged or socially vulnerable (e.g., ethnic or sexual minorities).
- Even in the very poorest countries with a significant array of major health issues, mental health problems are still a leading cause of both disability and loss of economic productivity.
- Global mental health resources tend to be in scarce supply in all countries relative to the health burden they generate, but they are especially unavailable in very poor countries where as many as half of sufferers go untreated.
- Global mental health resources are inequitably distributed across rich and poor nations and communities, and between urban and rural areas.
- Stigmatization, discrimination, and human rights abuses are common afflictions for people with mental health diseases,

> which amplify suffering; stigmatization is also suffered by family members and mental health care providers because of their association with this defamed population. (Lancet Series on Global Mental Health 2005)

SYNDEMICS

Historically, there were three key disease-related terms in epidemiology and public health: **epidemic** (a noticeable increase in the number of cases of a particular disease within a population), **pandemic** (the spread of a disease across human populations within a region, multiple regions, or worldwide), and **endemic** (a disease that remains in a population over a long period of time). During the 1990s, a fourth disease concept, initially developed by anthropologist Merrill Singer, has been adopted by a growing number of people working in medical anthropology, public health, medicine, and other health-related disciplines (Singer 2009b). This new concept is **syndemic**, which refers to the adverse interaction between two or more diseases resulting in an increased health burden for the affected population that is greater than the sum of the negative health impacts of each of the involved diseases. An example is the frequent co-occurrence and mutually enhancing interaction of HIV/AIDS infection, malnutrition, tuberculosis, and a set of other diseases among the poor of southern Africa. These diseases and health conditions impact people in the region not as a set of independent epidemics but rather as interacting components of a single devastating syndemic. The additional disease burden introduced by syndemics is a product of biological, behavioral, or other interfaces that take place among comorbid diseases. In the case of southern Africa, the Burden of Disease Study found that

> population health has declined rapidly in the last decade as evidenced by a decreasing life expectancy. This has been a result of the rapid spread of an HIV epidemic of profound proportion. The AIDS epidemic has fuelled the TB epidemic and also resulted in increased deaths due to pneumonia, diarrhea and other indicator conditions. (Bradshaw and Nannan 2003:47)

People infected with HIV who are exposed to the bacteria that cause tuberculosis are 800 times more likely than people not infected with HIV to develop active TB. This occurs because of the severe damage HIV does to the immune system by destroying key components like CD4 cells, the "helper" cells that facilitate the body's defensive response to infections (Lockman et al. 2003). At the same time, TB infection speeds the progression of HIV infection. In short, in the words of Lee Jong-wook, former director-general of the WHO (2004b:1) "TB/HIV is a deadly combination."

Another contributor to disease burden is malnutrition, which exacerbates the effects of many diseases. In southern Africa it plays a major role in facilitating the progression of HIV, TB, and other infections by weakening the body's ability to contain infectious disease. This same pattern is seen in the case of leprosy, which continues to spread in endemic countries like Bangladesh. Research there by Sabiena Feenstra and colleagues (2011) found a direct association between a period of food shortage and an increase in identified new leprosy infections, most likely because inadequate nutrient intake during the period of enhanced food insecurity reduced cell-mediated immunity in individuals who had been infected with the pathogen, *Mycobacterium leprae*, the cause of leprosy. Several contemporary examples of syndemics include the interaction of HIV and helminth infections, SARS and chronic diseases like cardiovascular conditions, depression and diabetes, and influenza and asthma. A list of syndemics already described in the health literature is far longer (see Singer 2009b).

A focus on syndemics highlights the fundamental importance of the interaction of the biological and the social in disease. Syndemics occur in no small part because of the unhealthy social conditions that promote the spread of disease and the concentration or clustering of particular diseases in vulnerable populations. Consequently, significant syndemics are found disproportionately among subordinated groups and populations as a direct consequence of their unequal social status and treatment within society. Building on but moving beyond epidemiological concepts like comorbidity and epidemic, "a syndemics framework describes situations in which adverse social conditions, such as poverty[,] . . . oppressive social relationships [and a degraded environment] stress a population, weaken its natural defenses, and expose it to a cluster of diseases" (Mendenhall 2011:2–3). Syndemics, because of the enhanced health burden they produce, further tip the scales of global health inequality against poor, disadvantaged, and socially marginalized populations and create significant additional challenges for the achievement of global health.

GLOBALIZATION AND HEALTH

Beyond anthropogenic reshaping of the environment, a second global force that significantly impacts human health is economic globalization, also of human origin. Malcolm Waters describes globalization as the "creation of new economic, financial, political, cultural, and personal relationships through which societies and nations come into closer and novel types of contact with one another" (2001:8). Driving this worldwide social transformation is a set of transnational capitalist economic processes, including a global market, rapidly evolving digital and communication technologies, and the movement of capital across national boundaries. One consequence of such movement is the restructuring of social life and experience (e.g., Warlpiri diet and identity) at home (e.g., as factories are built along border regions, such as that between the United States and Mexico) and abroad (e.g., as workers cross regional and national boundaries in search of work).

In a globalized world, multiple entities—including commodities (e.g., food, snack products, and drugs), people (e.g., migrants, refugees), lifestyles (e.g. global youth culture), and diseases (including both infectious diseases and chronic diseases)—move quickly and widely. Thus, "Coca-Cola and Hershey's chocolate [are found] in Manila as well as in New York" (Whiteford and Manderson 2000:3)—cities separated by geography, history, culture, language, and disease profiles. These flows, and the ways in which they interact with local conditions and responses, have significant and multifaceted consequences for global human health and well-being.

While there are health benefits of globalization, such as the greater availability of medicines in developing countries and the increased availability of complementary and alternative medical systems, many global health analysts conclude that on balance, for poor nations, globalization further advances health inequality. A case in point is the global flow of commercial tobacco products. WHO (2001) estimates that the death toll from tobacco use will reach 10 million a year by 2020. Almost three-quarters of these deaths, from lung cancer, cardiovascular diseases, respiratory diseases, and diabetes, will occur in developing countries because tobacco companies target people in poor nations as potential new sources of profit, to replace those quitting smoking in developed nations. Alcohol consumption, especially among young people, is another area in which globalization enhances global health risks. While alcohol and tobacco are legal drugs, illegal drugs like heroin and cocaine also flow more freely in a world of enhanced commodity movement across more porous borders, as do drug-related threats to health such as HIV/AIDS, hepatitis, and overdose (Singer 2008).

Part and parcel of globalization are **neoliberalism** and **structural adjustment policies (SAPs),** concepts that were discussed briefly in chapter 1. Neoliberalism is an economic philosophy that maintains that the market, and not governments, should determine the price of goods, including food staples, medicines, education, health care, and housing. Neoliberal policies have led to significant jumps in prices and loss of access to health care in many developing nations, loss of jobs, and further impoverization and its associated health burdens. International lending institutions argued that the pains of adjustments would be short term. But, writing of sub-Saharan Africa, anthropologist Brook Schoepf and coworkers argue "Africa's working poor have been made to endure wage freezes, unemployment, hunger, and ill-health so that funds might be directed to pay foreign debts and restore or enhance corporate profitability. [As a result] SAPs mean that for many poor Africans *there will be no long term*" (2000:125).

CONCLUSION

Health is a product of multiple intersecting biological, environmental, and sociocultural factors. An examination of global health patterns, however, affirms that some influences are particularly important. In this chapter, we have highlighted the impact of global warming and other anthropogenic environmental degradations on health issues; the globalization of infectious diseases, noncommunicable chronic diseases, and mental health; and the role global forces play in exacerbating social and economic inequality and their health effects. Within this framework, we have emphasized a more complex way of understanding the particular health consequences of the interaction of diseases (syndemics) within the context of multiple interacting environmental contexts (pluralea).

In closing, we add that pluralea can contribute to the development of syndemics. For example, global warming and air pollution interact to promote asthma and adverse infectious disease interactions, which are exacerbated by socioeconomic conditions. This is an **ecosyndemic**, an environmentally mediated adverse interaction of two or more diseases that increase the human health burden. Given the fundamental role of human actions in generating these interactions and the importance of culture and structures of social relationship in shaping human responses to their health consequences, the value of the anthropological paradigm is further revealed.

A critical lesson for public health, the health social sciences, and medicine is that global health efforts must be grounded in a biosocial, syndemic, and ecosyndemic model of health and disease that pays attention to the critical role of health inequities and the cultural patterns and lived-experiences of populations that suffer the consequences of globalization and anthropogenic climate change. Anthropology is a holistic social science that looks at multiple levels of causation and cure. In our globalized world, we cannot ignore the complex and mutually reinforcing interactions among disease, environment, culture, and society.

Notes

[1] The Saffir-Simpson Hurricane Scale categorizes storms into five categories based on wind speed and storm surge. Category 1 is the lowest with wind speeds of 74–95 miles per hour and 4–5 foot surges. Category 5 is the highest with wind speeds of 156 or more miles per hour and surges of 18 feet or more.

[2] The infant mortality rate is the number of children under one year of age who die per 1,000 live births.

[3] Ozone is known as a secondary pollutant because it is formed when nitrogen oxides and volatile organic compounds from motor vehicle exhaust or industrial emissions combine in the presence of heat and sunlight.

Chapter Four

Basic Survival Needs and Their Privatization

Lawrence Gostin, director of the Global Health Law Program at the Georgetown University Law Center, maintains that health depends on meeting **basic survival needs**, including sanitation and sewage processing, pest control, clean air and water, adequate diet and nutrition, access to essential medicines and vaccines, and availability of a functioning health system. Meeting these everyday needs of existence, he acknowledges, "may lack the glamour of high-technology medicine or dramatic rescue, but what they lack in excitement they gain in their potential impact on health, precisely because they deal with the major causes of common disease and disabilities across the globe" (Gostin 2008:331). In this chapter, we address several of the basic survival needs noted by Gostin, specifically adequate food, clean and sufficient water, and access to a functioning health care system, with a focus on maternal and child health care as a foundational component of public health.

DIET AND HEALTH IN HUMAN HISTORY

Diet adequacy "may be the single most important determinant of health" (Schoepf 2000:112). This is so because insufficient nutrition is damaging to human health in its own right and because poor nutrition and disease are synergistic; "the presence of either increases the likelihood of the other" (Schoepf 2000:112). As Sidney Mintz and Christine Du Bois emphasize, "Next to breathing, eating is perhaps the most essential of all human activities, and one with which much of social life is entwined" (2002:102).

For the first several million years of human history (a period known as the Paleolithic Age) in all inhabited regions of the world, food came from the wild plants people could gather and the animals they could hunt. Societies organized around the foraging of undomesticated food sources tended to be small, mobile and egalitarian in their access to food. When food was plentiful everyone ate (cultural rules ensured food distribution within the group); when it was scarce (because of drought or some other natural cause) the whole group suffered. No doubt, under such uncertain conditions, at times some small bands died off because they could not provision themselves. This way of life persisted for millions of years, and it is likely that, on the whole, prehistoric foragers were capable of feeding themselves adequately most of the time. This conclusion is supported by archeological analyses of skeletal remains of Paleolithic peoples showing that their nutritional health was excellent (Cohen and Armelagos 1984).

Approximately 10,000 years ago, however, people began cultivating plants and domesticating local animals (a transition known as the Neolithic Revolution). Reliance on horticultural food production did not emerge because of the sudden discovery of how to cultivate plants or domesticate animals (because to survive, foragers needed to know the traits of local plant and animal species extremely well) or because it allowed for an easier way of life with more food for everyone. Rather, it was likely the consequence of changes in environmental conditions (e.g., a less hospitable climate) or the overhunting of large animals that pressed human groups in some areas to try to gain more control over their food sources or face starvation.

Initially, the addition of cultivated food plants to the human diet probably did not have an immediate dramatic effect on human society. Over time, however, Neolithic diets increasingly focused on calorie-rich but protein-limited starchy food sources (i.e., grains and root crops). With food cultivation, and especially the domestication of herd animals, the potential for social inequalities in access to food emerged because it could be stored and hence controlled by an elite class. A classic book, *Paleopathology at the Origins of Agriculture* (Cohen and Armelagos 1984), examined this issue in detail. Evidence for inequality in food access comes from fossil teeth that had enamel hypoplasias and carbohydrate-related tooth disease suggesting that some people (primarily nonelites) were not eating adequate diets. While population size grew because of sufficient carbohydrates, in many environments people were no longer as well fed as their Paleolithic ancestors.

With the subsequent Industrial Revolution—another far-reaching transition in human ways of life—people began to move into cities and adopt urban lifestyles. Many poor people were forced to live in urban slums characterized by unhealthy conditions and very inadequate diets. Part and parcel of industrialization and urbanization was the conversion of food into a commodity that had to be purchased in the marketplace rather than hunted, gathered, or farmed. Today, food is not something most people produce to eat themselves but something corporations sell to make a profit. The best agricultural lands are now used for growing crops (e.g., coffee, tobacco, sugar cane) that bring in the highest prices and biggest profits for the wealthiest social classes rather than crops that produce affordable food that meets people's basic nutritional needs. In this world, hunger has become an enduring feature of life for many people. Moreover, the contemporary food crisis unites undernutrition (starvation, hunger, and nutritional deficiency diseases) and overnutrition (overconsumption of obesogenic, high carbohydrate processed foods) within and between nations.

KNOWING HUNGER

WHO (World Food Program 2012) reports the following statistical overview of hunger in the modern world: One of every seven people does not get enough food to enable him or her to feel healthy and to lead an active and secure life. Indeed, hunger is now the single greatest risk to health in the world and the cause of death for more than the combined number of deaths due to the "big three" human infectious diseases on the planet: AIDS, malaria, and tuberculosis. A combination of the total populations of the US, Canada, and the European Union would not equal the number of people in the world who are hungry. While women comprise a little over half of the world's population, they account for over 60 percent of the world's hungry, and many more suffer food insecurity. Moreover, undernutrition contributes to five million child deaths (under age five) in developing countries annually, or almost 15,000 a day, and one of four children living in developing countries (just under 150 million children) is underweight for his or her age. More than 70 percent of these underweight children live in just ten less developed countries. Iron deficiency is the most frequent form of malnutrition worldwide, currently affecting as many as two billion people. Iodine deficiency, the single most important cause of mental retardation and brain damage, also impacts two billion people. As this grave itemization of food-related health problems suggests, food issues are of critical importance in shaping global health and involve a number of components: hunger, malnutrition, undernutrition, and food insecurity. Each of these and related terms are defined and further discussed below.

- **Hunger** is a biological signaling system built into our bodies to alert us if we are running low on ingested food. While short-term hunger is not a health issue, prolonged hunger can lead to body-damaging malnutrition.
- **Malnutrition** is a physical state in which lack of adequate protein and/or calories and micronutrients damages normal functioning of the body's natural abilities, such that growth, pregnancy, lactation, learning, work, and resisting and recovering from infection are impaired. The term covers a range of food-related health problems, from being notably underweight, to having stunted growth, to being deficient in specific vitamins and minerals (undernutrition), to being overweight or obese (overnutrition). According to the UN System Standing Committee on Nutrition (2004), almost one-third of all children in the world suffer from stunting due to undernutrition. Furthermore, the deaths of 3.7 million children under the age of five are associated with their own or their mother's underweight status (Ezzati et al. 2004). Another expression of malnutrition is wasting, which is recent acute loss of weight. Undernourishment in a child can begin before conception with poor pre-pregnancy BMI (Body Mass Index)[1] in the expectant mother. Undernourishment is intensified by maternal inadequate diet and weight gain during pregnancy and compromised milk production after birth. These deficits often result in low birth weight and poor weight gain during infancy. This burden can be further exacer-

Poverty, malnutrition, and poor housing in Cité Soliel, Haiti. (Merrill Singer)

bated by the child's poor subsequent nutritional status and the quantity of available food, especially after weaning. Even among children who survive, the adverse effects of these multiple challenges can be life-long: "Chronic undernutrition, especially in conjunction with poor environmental stimulation, is associated with impaired cognitive development, and severe undernutrition during infancy may contribute to lasting intellectual deficits" (Fishman et al. 2004:41).

- **Food insecurity** refers to the urgent "food problem" of the contemporary world. The term was introduced at the first World Food Conference in 1974 that focused on increasing the food supply and ensuring the flow of basic staples at reasonable prices for all people (Pottier 1999). With the publication of *Poverty and Famines*, attention shifted to the political-economic causes of famine (Sen 1981). Amartya Sen carefully demonstrated that people do not suffer food insecurity solely from a lack of available food but because of social inequalities built into food distribution systems. The primary lesson is that the commodification of food undermines the food security of the poor when there is a rapid increase in social and economic inequality (Maxwell and Fernando 1989).

UNDERSTANDING FOOD INSECURITY: THE ANTHROPOLOGICAL APPROACH

Food insecurity is a broad term that draws attention to the relationship between food and people's survival and well-being. Most international efforts intended to combat food insecurity have been guided by quantitative indicators. While such measures are useful in understanding the extent of food insecurity, anthropologists see a lack of fit between the lived-experiences among those who suffer food shortages and the general understandings that have informed policy makers. Consequently, anthropologists advocate the addition of grounded, community-centered approaches to gain an understanding of specific local attitudes and experiences (e.g., people's perceptions of the sources of food problems), local factors in food insecurity (e.g., local patterns of coping), and the enmeshment of local conditions in global processes (e.g., rising global food prices).

Anthropologists maintain that rather than top-down initiatives that rely on outside experts who are rarely aware of local conditions, "intervention programs that are based on an understanding of the local cultural, social, ecological, and political-economic conditions generally tend to be effective and sustainable" (Khanna 2012:198). This is the approach anthropologists have brought to their work on food (in)security issues at institutions like the FAO, the US Department of Agriculture, the National Oceanic and Atmosphere Administration, USAID, International Food Policy Research Institute, the Cooperative for Assistance and Relief Everywhere, and WHO. They have also advocated for access to food as a basic human right.

From an anthropological standpoint, averting local food insecurity requires: (1) an understanding of how communities produce or acquire food, (2) the ways they protect themselves from famine and cope with barriers to food access, and (3) the physical and social structural factors that make people nutritionally vulnerable. The first of these rests on a long-standing anthropological recognition that the successful introduction of social change requires a detailed understanding of what it is you are trying to change. As Benjamin Paul noted long ago,

> Before asking a group of people to assume new health habits [like food production, acquisition, and use patterns], it is wise to ascertain the existing habits, how these habits are linked to one another . . . and what they mean to those who practice them. (1955:1)

Food is never merely a resource to address bodily needs; it is simultaneously a basis for cultural identity and social solidarity. Eating itself is a social behavior imbued with a rich complex of cultural meanings and deep emotional attachments and memories. Anthropologists argue that it is critical to determine the distribution of power relationships within food systems and how decisions about food production and distribution are made. Anthropologists have tended to emphasize a community-based approach to understanding indigenous knowledge about food and the social organization of food-related behaviors.

The second element entails examination of how communities and households respond to food crises. In Mozambique, for example, Miriam Chaiken and coworkers (2009) identified a number of culturally constituted practices that reflected indigenous efforts to limit the impact of local food shortages, including the addition or expansion of wild foods to what had become primarily a domesticated food diet; the inclusion of less desirable foods (deemed untasty or difficult to digest); expansion of efforts to acquire even short-term, low-status, and poorly paying jobs (e.g., hiring out their labor to prosperous neighbors) to get enough money to purchase food; engaging in illegal activities to increase food access (including stealing food); lowering household food demand by reducing household size (e.g., sending children away to live with family members in other areas); and reducing food demand by limiting the frequency of meals (down from three to two or one per day). Identification of these strategies affirms the importance of culturally informed agency and local decision making in the context of a food crisis.

Anthropologists have made significant contributions to an ethnographic understanding of the pathways through which political-economic inequality translates into food insecurity and the ways people cope with the resulting loss of life, especially of children. Based on her fieldwork in Northeast Brazil, Nancy Scheper-Hughes (1992) examined the stoic responses of mothers to food-related child death. Because of chronic food insufficiency among poor working families in this sugar plantation region and the need to make grim household decisions about how to distribute scarce food, mothers are prepared for small children to die and may even assist in this process with babies who early on appear to be listless and seemingly lack the will to live.

SOCIAL FACTORS THAT CAUSE FOOD INSECURITY

Within the broader context of global social inequality, we now introduce additional social factors that exacerbate food insecurity.

Industrialization of Farming

In the period after the Second World War, there was a push among Western nations to help "modernize" agricultural practices in underdeveloped countries to expand productivity. A less public agenda was to incorporate local farmers into the international market, thereby blocking the appeal of socialism, which was of growing interest in less developed countries during this period (Singer 2008b).

This initiative, called the **Green Revolution**, began in Mexico and spread worldwide by the 1960s. The worldview underlying the Green Revolution held that traditional non-Western agricultural systems were not based on modern agroscience and were, thus, primitive, inefficient, ultimately destructive, and in need of modernization (Wainwright 2008). The solution was the introduction of corporate-owned high-yield, fast-maturing crop seeds, use of mechanized technologies, and the adoption of commercial agrochemicals (e.g., fertilizers, pesticides, and herbicides sold as commodities). In India, for example, a country that was facing widespread famine at the beginning of the 1960s, this approach seemed to work in that the introduction of a new patented rice variety and other industrial changes enabled a significant expansion of food production. Within a few years, however, the number of available rice varieties shrank from over 30,000 to just ten. With this degree of concentrated monocrop agriculture (and severe loss of biodiversity), insects and other pests adapted, and their eradication required the use of more powerful pesticides.

The Punjab region (known as the breadbasket of India) was selected by the Indian government to be the initial site of its Green

Revolution because of its history of success in food production. While the new techniques led to notable jumps in productivity, problems began to appear locally. Water costs also increased and farmers realized that the heavy use of agrochemicals required by high-yield seeds was expensive, degraded the environment, and led to soil nutrient depletion. They also began to question the impact of agrochemicals on health, with rising rates of cancer magnifying popular concern (Faridkot/Muktsar 2012). Some farmers resented the tight control agribusiness kept on their seeds, forcing them to buy new seeds each year rather than plant rice from the prior year's harvest, the traditional pattern. In time, the high costs of the Green Revolution drove many small farmers deeply into debt, leading to the loss of family farms and further widening the significant social and economic disparities of Indian society. Debt, loss of independence, and uncertainty led to a significant jump in the rate of suicides among small farmers in India (Mohanty 2005). Ultimately, a growing number of farmers viewed the Green Revolution as unsustainable and began to look to organic farming and other sustainable methods.

Summing up the criticisms of the Green Revolution's agro-techno-fix approach to the world food crisis, internationally known food and sustainability activist Vandana Shiva (1991), a leader in the organic farming and alternative seed bank initiatives in India, argues:

> The Green Revolution has been a failure. . . . The beneficiaries have been the agrochemical industry, large petrochemical companies, manufacturers of agricultural machinery, dam builders and large landowners.

While Green Revolution supporters discount this assertion, there is no denying that world hunger has increased, especially in India, home to the world's largest food insecure population according to the International Food Policy Research Institute (2011).

Poverty and Food Price Volatility

In a world of global connectedness, characterized by the movement of vast quantities of food commodities around the world, the price of food is highly volatile, going up or down each year. But, since 2002, the UN's food price index has shown that food prices have generally trended upward. As a result, a poor family in a low-income country may be forced to spend as much as 75 percent of its income on food. In 2008, a sudden steep jump in food prices led to food riots in over 25 countries. In Bangladesh, workers in Dhaka attacked factories in angry protest over suddenly higher food prices and continued low wages. In Haiti, where the price of basic food staples jumped by 50 percent, outraged protesters attempted to break into the presidential palace to demand the president's resignation (Ryan 2008). While emergency government actions led to a temporary drop in food prices, they began to rise again in 2010.

Various factors contributed to the rise in food prices, including increased fuel prices and the expanding biofuels market. Crops, like corn, can be converted into motor vehicle fuel rather than using it for food. Increased demand for meat in some wealthy countries or those with expanding economies like China is displacing food grown for people with food grown to support meat production, which many people in the world cannot afford. In addition, climate change—in part a product of burning more fuel—is contributing to droughts that lower global food production. Food-price speculation, which involves wealthy investors buying food futures with hopes that prices and profits will go up, also destabilizes food prices (Smith 2012). Additionally, structural adjustment policies (SAPs, discussed in chapter 3) have resulted in rising food costs and increasing hunger, and in some instances, as in parts of India, starvation (Swaminathan 1996). Howard Rosing's ethnographic study of SAPs in the Dominican Republic (2012:72) concluded that such policies "resulted in displacement of rural livelihoods, unfettered urbanization, and immiseration," while contributing to the global food crisis.

Gender Discrimination

One form of food insecurity has been labeled "hidden hunger," often caused by gender-based inequalities in access to food. In many societies, rural-dwelling women are more likely to be directly involved in the cultivation of food than men (in all world regions except the Middle East and North Africa), and in most they are also responsible for feeding family members. In sub-Saharan Africa, for example, women grow 80–90 percent of the locally produced food (Weisfield-Adams 2008). Consequently, women are seen as key to food security for their households (Quisumbing et al. 1995), but not necessarily for themselves. The burden of filling multiple household roles—which often include transport of water and fuel in addition to food production, food processing, and child care—puts a significant burden on women, especially in the least developed countries. Moreover, women are often denied access to land except through male relatives and often do not have the same access to food as men. In the Haitian capital, for example, Catherine Maternowska (2006) found that all but two of the 42 Haitian women she interviewed mentioned malnutrition as one of the most common health problems they face. Observed Maternowska, "Women are required to feed their husbands and children before they eat themselves. . . . [While] the Food and Agricultural Organization (FAO) estimates that 62 percent of the population are undernourished . . . it is estimated that women suffer considerably more than men in this respect" (2006:61).

War and Disease

One in every ten reported violent deaths around the world occurs in conflict settings. There is a close association between human conflict and food challenges, a relationship that has been called "food wars." It involves intentionally causing hunger, especially for the civilians on the other side of a conflict (Messer 1998, 2012). In fact, a significant portion of the toll on human lives during contemporary armed conflicts is caused either by disease or by the loss of access to food inside war zones (Human Security Research Group 2009). The Geneva Declaration Secretariat's (2008) report, "Global Burden of Armed Violence," estimates that for every individual killed by violence during wars between 2004 and 2007 (about 600,000), another four (2,4000,000) fell to war-related disease and malnutrition. Significantly, research in Mozambique has shown that the death of an adult, whatever the cause, reduces the amount of staple foods his or her household produced by 20–30 percent and contributes significantly to household food insecurity (Donovan and Massingue 2007). In this light, armed conflict has come to be recognized as one of the most important sources of contemporary food insecurity. Infectious diseases, especially endemic conditions (e.g., intestinal worm) and epidemics (e.g., HIV/AIDS) that take significant tolls on the lives and productive capacities of a population, are also significant drivers of food insecurity (Singer 2011b). This fateful relationship is termed the "nutrition-infection complex" (Scrimshaw and San Giovanni 1997).

A HUMAN RIGHTS APPROACH TO FOOD INSECURITY

Belief that access to food is a basic human right has a long history. It is codified in the United Nations Universal Declaration of Human Rights issued just after World War II. Article 25 of the document states that "everyone has the right to a standard of living adequate for health and well-being of himself and his family, including food." As Ellen Messer and Marc Cohen (2009) report, "The significance of freedom of speech, a free press, and freedom of assembly for the protection of economic rights, including the right not to starve, connects food security to democracy and good governance."

The human rights approach to food insecurity has gained considerable support in developing countries. In 2003, Brazil, for example, adopted its Zero Hunger strategy, an effort to combat poverty. As part of this initiative, a law was passed requiring the government to enforce the universal right to regular and permanent access to good quality food in sufficient quantities to ensure health (Ananias 2009). As a result of this and other changes, Brazil has reported significant drops in poverty and food insecurity in recent years, although great disparities in wealth, health, and access to food continue.

Is the Human Rights Approach Working? As the United Nations Food and Agriculture Organization (FAO) stresses, "It is a bitter irony that as developing countries continue their efforts to reduce hunger, some are also facing the opposing problem of obesity" (2002). The number of overweight individuals in both developed and developing nations is surpassing the number of underweight individuals. Incongruously, obesity is growing even in countries with significant hunger problems. In developing nations like Brazil and Colombia, as much as 40 percent of the population is overweight. Pacific Island nations like Tonga, Samoa, and Nauru have even higher rates of obesity, hitting over 75 percent. Even sub-Saharan Africa, with its significant hunger problem, is witnessing a jump in obesity. Rising rates of obesity confirm that the world produces enough food to feed everyone.

HEALTH AND THE GLOBAL WATER CRISIS

Less than one percent of the water on our planet is fresh water—in lakes, rivers, streams, or underground aquifers—available for drinking. The rest is found in the oceans, the levels of which are rising due to global warming. Our global hydraulic system is a closed one: the total amount of water remains the same whether it is found in the oceans, glaciers, permafrost, lakes, rivers, or polluted pools. The amount of water people use has changed significantly over the two million years that *Homo sapiens* has lived on the planet. Estimates of the amount of water needed for drinking and sanitation per person per day vary according to climate, but on average it is 50 liters per capita per day (Gleick 1996). Agriculture and industry use a lot of water. About 71 percent of the fresh water is used by agricultural irrigation and another 22 percent by industry (World Business Council for Sustainable Development 2011). Thus, the amount of water available for drinking and other household uses is quite limited.

The amount of fresh water needed by humans has increased with our growing global population and our changing means of exploiting Earth's resources. The human population reached seven billion in October 2011, and UN demographers project it may reach nine billion in 2045. Moreover, especially since the Industrial Revolution, we began contaminating our fresh water resources beyond their natural cleansing capabilities. Water is the next scarce resource, and the water wars have just begun.

As anthropologists Linda Whiteford and Cecilia Vindrola Padros observe, "It is difficult to fully comprehend our constant and pervasive dependence on water, particularly for those of us who live where we have easy and reliable access to clean water" (2011:204). Access to uncontaminated water for drinking and sanitary purposes is a fundamental precondition for human health and well-being, while lack of access is a significant source of global ill-health. Today, one-sixth of the world's population lacks safe drinking water, and more than double this number lacks even basic sanitation facilities (WHO 2005c). This means that only one in five children in developing countries have access to safe drinking water, resulting in 1.4 million child deaths each year—one every 15 seconds from water-related diseases (UNICEF 2005). Contaminated water and poor sanitation are the immediate causes of almost 90 percent of child deaths annually from diarrheal diseases, which are the second largest cause of global child mortality (Watkins 2006). Other diseases of inadequate sanitation include dysentery, cholera, hepatitis, typhoid, and parasitic infections. Overall, water-related infectious diseases claim over three million lives annually (Corvalan 2005). It is well-known that improvement in water supply and sanitation can dramatically decrease such mortality statistics (Watkins 2006).

Overcoming this global water crisis is one of the great human development and global health challenges we face in the first half of the twenty-first century. If current trends persist, it is estimated that by 2025 there will be three billion people without an adequate supply of drinkable water (Rosegrant et al. 2002). This projection is rarely reflected in news media, nor is it often a focus of international planning. Yet, the global water crisis is a major threat to world stability as tensions over water can quickly turn into violent conflict. Consequently, safe and adequate water supply has emerged as an "urgent theme" in contemporary health-related anthropology (Orlove and Canton 2010:401).

As we have seen with other health issues, there is tremendous disparity within and across nations in access to clean water and sanitation. In the developed nations, all but the very poor usually have access to safe water in adequate supply, although

> as many as 19 million Americans may become ill each year due to . . . parasites, viruses and bacteria in [their contaminated municipal] drinking water. Certain types of cancer—such as breast and prostate cancer—have risen over the past 30 years, and research indicates they are likely tied to pollutants like those found in drinking water. (Duhigg 2009)

Those with the least access to clean water survive as the bottom billion of the world's population earning less than $2 per day. They are subject to what has been called **stratified hygiene**. For example, anthropologist Eric Stein studied sanitation in a rural Indonesia village and found that wealthier households could afford indoor plumbing and those who could not tended to be "primarily landless sharecroppers, pedicab drivers and other day laborers, or small landowners farming remote hillside plots . . . [for] low-value staples" (2009:553–554). While better-off families lived in houses made of cement blocks and had wells and running water, the homes of poorer families were made of bamboo, had dirt floors, and lacked toilet access. Stein also found a prioritization of global and national sanitation policies and the failure of including impoverished families within health education campaigns, combined with a prevailing attitude of blaming the victims of stratified sanitation for their failure to "be modern" in their hygienic practices.

Failed global and national water and sanitation policies result in intense water-related health calamities. This occurred in 2008 in Harare, Zimbabwe, in southern Africa when the municipal water system failed and disease spread as people turned to other, often contaminated sources of water. According to one local observer during the crisis, "People are dying at an alarming rate. There are funeral wakes in many households. The government might try to deny this, but the reality is there for all to see" (Inter Press Service 2008). Health rights groups, such as the Zimbabwe Doctors for Human Rights, estimated the death toll from the crisis numbered in the thousands and as many as 20,000 people contracted the water-borne disease cholera.

Globally, gender is also a critical factor in water issues, as women and girls "carry a double burden of disadvantage" (Watkins 2006:2). On the one hand, in water-insecure areas of the world they often have to spend many hours each day retrieving water for their households, sometimes from distant sources, taking time away from other activities, such as pursuing an education or learning survival skills. Through their greater involvement in domestic work, such as washing dishes and clothes in rivers and lakes, women may be put at greater risk for water-borne infections like schistosomiasis, a parasitic disease that damages the liver, kidneys, and other vital organs and is believed to put sufferers at higher risk for HIV infection (WHO 2009). It is estimated that 45 million girls and women in sub-Saharan Africa alone are infected with schistosomiasis.

Finally, there is the issue of culture, which is deeply entwined with all of the other factors mentioned above. In a classic paper in medical anthropology, Edward Wellin (1955) analyzed the challenges faced by public health workers trying to persuade residents of a rural Peruvian town to boil water before consuming it, thus reducing rates of water-borne diseases. Water boiling makes sense to those fully immersed in a biomedical model of infectious diseases, but "perceptions of . . . water are culturally screened" (Wellin 1955:100); hearing about water-borne pathogens and how to control them does not replace people's preexisting understandings of disease causation (e.g., because of body imbalances or conflict within one's social group). Barriers to water boiling included both cultural and practical issues: boiled water was thought to be appropriate only for the sick, and fuel was costly in terms of time taken to gather it. Thus, women resisted boiling water for daily use.

A common reaction among health workers who experience resistance to the biomedical model of hygiene is to blame the local people for being ignorant and stubborn. As the story about water boiling suggests, however, resistance to a new way of doing things may result from local health-related **cultural logics** of disease causation that are not based on germ theory. Behaviors associated with alternative theories of disease make sense in their local cultural context. They are often integrated with local social relationship structures and shared understandings of physical reality that are threatened by externally introduced models. At the same time, considerable research supports the realization that people can embrace, integrate, and act on ideas and practices from diverse sources, such as hybrid ideas about water and health. Thus, culture is neither an ironclad barrier to health improvement nor an insignificant factor that can be ignored in health development initiatives such as water improvement and sanitation programs. Moreover, culture is not the only factor, as the case of water boiling in Peru illustrates. Water boiling was both culturally and economically incompatible with local beliefs, available resources and technologies, and ways of living.

Barriers to Water Access

Is access to clean water and sanitation simply a result of where you happen to live? Or is differential access the result of economic inequities whereby some people are simply able to pay more for water than others? Analyses of the global water crisis, in fact, have reached very different conclusions depending on which perspective you take. There is abundant evidence that a scarcity of clean water "is manufactured through political processes and institutions that disadvantage the poor" (Watkins 2006:3). Ironically, the poor often pay more for water than their wealthy counterparts but lack the political power to ensure full value for their payment. For example, a study by the United Nations Development Programme (2006) found that people living in the slums of Manila, Philippines, pay more for their water than middle-class residents of London.

In *Globalization, Water, and Health*, anthropologists Linda Whiteford and Scott Whiteford (2005) explore how globalization reshapes health and environmental policies, stressing the need to look at the interaction of human culture, environmental resources, and social power as an encompassing global relationship that shapes access to water. As Whiteford and Padros comment, "what people believe about water (and about health) is culturally created, but it is also shaped by global economic and political forces, as well as environmental factors" (2011:204). A case in point is the pollution of the Ganges River in India.

CASE STUDY
Contamination of the Ganges

The Ganges River—the sacred river of Hinduism believed to have restorative powers—is a critical source of sustenance for millions of Indians. The basin of the river is one of the most populated areas on Earth, containing 450 million people. The Ganges is also one of the ten most polluted rivers in the world. In 1986, the prime minister of India acknowledged this, noting: "the dirt of the city, of industry, of factories and of dead animals—we are throwing into the Ganga" (quoted in Alley 2002:36). Human, industrial, agricultural, and urban wastewater flows into the Ganges all along its route. Pollution has become so extensive that using river water for drinking and bathing—daily activities for millions—has become a health risk.

A significant source of pollution is the almost one billion liters of largely untreated raw sewage that enters the river daily. Most of the sewage (about 350 million gallons a day) is produced by the 30 cities and over 70 towns along its banks. Agricultural pollution adds another six million tons of chemical fertilizers and 9,000 tons of pesticides annually. The major industrial polluting agent is the leather industry, especially near the city of Kanpur in the industrial heartland of the state of Uttar Pradesh, where chromium and other toxic chemicals are dumped into the river (World Wildlife Fund 2003). While government health reports suggest that to be safe for drinking the river water should contain no more than 2 mg per liter of chromium, tests show that in some places it contains 150–170 mg per liter. Chromium is classified as a carcinogen (e.g., skin cancer) and a cause of kidney and liver damage, chronic bronchitis, and ulcers.

Pharmaceutical companies, electronics plants, textile and paper manufacturers, and oil refineries also discharge effluent into the Ganges. These industries dump hydrochloric acid, mercury and other heavy metals, bleaches and dyes, polychlorinated biphenyls, and other highly toxic compounds into the river. Collectively, powerful industries have been able to resist most government efforts to regulate their release of toxins into the Ganges. A study of 42 tanneries in Uttar Pradesh found that despite the existence of strong environmental laws, enforcement is poor because of corruption (e.g., bribing regulators) (Schjolden 2000). As is often the case, water contamination is not simply a lack of knowledge or protective policies but reflects the relative political power of those who contaminate and those who suffer from it. Climate change, too, is intensifying contaminant threats to the Ganges. Rising temperatures are melting away the glacial sources of the river's origin. As these water sources diminish, it will be an even greater challenge to supply the people of India with fresh water.

Water-Related Disasters

Another feature of water's critical role in human health is the part it plays in human disasters. As defined by WHO (1998), a disaster is "a serious disruption of the functioning of a community or a society causing widespread human, material, economic or environmental losses which exceed the ability of the affected community or society to cope using its own resources." A case in point was the tsunami, triggered by a major undersea earthquake in the Indian Ocean, on December 26, 2004. The tsunami carried enormous and powerful waves that inundated the coastal areas of most landmasses in the area. It is estimated that over 230,000 people were killed (a third of them children) in 14 countries, especially Indonesia (where most casualties occurred and half a million people were displaced), Sri Lanka, India, and Thailand, making it the single worst tsunami in history. A massive global humanitarian response followed, but even by 2012 many areas had not fully recovered. One of the suggested reasons that the tsunami was so devastating was the role of extensive human-caused damage (often intentional, but also as a result of ocean acidification and global warming) to natural barrier systems like coral reefs and the coastal mangroves and sand dunes that slow rushing ocean water (Browne 2004).

Of grave importance for global health, the worldwide incidence of human disasters is increasing. Notably, 40–50 percent of human disasters and 40–50 percent of disaster-related deaths are water-related (Du et al. 2010; Nicogossian et al. 2011). Further, as David McCann et al. stress, "Social determinants of health play a major role in water-related disasters because the poor, . . . the uneducated, . . . women, . . . the elderly, . . . the very young, . . . and the disabled . . . are more vulnerable" (2011:1). This is true for developed countries as well, as evidenced by the unequal impact of Hurricane Katrina on the poor of New Orleans in 2005.

HEALTH AND THE PRIVATIZATION OF WATER

The UN Universal Declaration of Human Rights (2002) declared: "Water is fundamental for life and health. The human right to water is indispensable for leading a healthy life in human dignity. It is a prerequisite to the realization of all other human rights." Environmental activist Vandana Shiva adds, "Since nature gives water to us free of cost, buying and selling it for profit violates our inherent right to nature's gift and denies the poor of their human rights" (2002:35–36). Water is intrinsically different from other resources and products. Traditionally, drinking water has been treated as a community "commons," that is, as a shared and valued resource with inherent equal public access based on community membership (Nonini 2007). This pattern has begun to change with potentially dire global health consequences. In an era of globalization and neoliberal privatization, governments, under pressure from global lending and development institutions like the World Bank, are abandoning their traditionally accepted responsibility for protecting the public good and the community commons. At the same time, for-profit corporations have been seeking ways to control commons resources, privatize them, and sell them as commodities for a profit. This involves adding water to the list of already privatized, but traditionally shared, natural resources (e.g., land, metal ore, diamonds, oil, ocean fish).

Troubling examples of the adverse consequences of privatization of water can be found in many countries around the world. A study by the International Consortium of Investigative Journalists (2003) found that the majority of World Bank development loans during the five years prior to their study required the conversion of public water systems into privately owned facilities as a condition for loan approval. The result in many parts of Europe and in the developing world has been significant profits for private companies, higher water prices for consumers, shutoffs for customers who cannot pay for water, and reduced water quality.

Examples include significant jumps in the cost of water in Senegal in the mid-1990s forcing citizens to turn to untreated water sources; the tripling of the cost of water in Bolivia following privatization just after the turn of the twentieth century; 20 percent increases in water prices for the city of Buenos Aires in 2002; and the shutoff of water to over ten million people in South Africa because they could not afford to pay for the newly privatized service, despite a constitutional guarantee of access to water for all (Barlow and Clarke 2004). Moreover, South African implementation of a water privatization policy in poor communities led to reduced access to safe water and contributed to the spread of cholera. Notes Barbara Rose Johnston, "more than two million South Africans were evicted from their homes—because they could not pay their water bill" (2005:146). People were forced to turn to streams, ponds and lakes for drinking water, some of which were polluted with manure and human waste, leading to a marked increase in waterborne diseases.

In the cases above, the essential issue is not the *availability* of clean water, but *access* to it, and the key to access is the power of private for-profit companies to control water distribution based on ability to pay. As Johnston argues, the transformation of water from a natural resource into a privately owned commodity is the "global imposition of a scarcity framework that uses the language and analytical tools of the market to assess water problems and to support preferred solutions" (2005:151). As an alternative, Johnston argues for a human rights–based approach that treats water as a public good. From this perspective, access to vital resources that are absolutely critical for human survival would be treated as government-enforced rights that cannot be hindered by the market, just as the government blocks a private company from buying up and publically selling the right to vote.

A related issue involves the international buying and bottling of clean water for sale. For example, in 2002 a company named PT Tirta Investama, a subsidiary of Danone, opened a plant in the Klaten district of Java in Indonesia. The majority of the people living there depend on wet-rice cultivation that relies on a spring-fed irrigation system during the dry season. With global warming, the dependability of spring water has diminished, and droughts have become more common, making water an increasingly tense issue for local people. Danone began extracting water for bottling from Sigedang spring, just 20 meters from the area's primary water source. Before long, local residents found that their access to irrigation water dramatically decreased as their wells started to run dry. Some residents were forced to stop farming and to seek other means of livelihood. In 2003, community members came together to establish an organization called the Klaten People's Coalition for Justice to advocate on their behalf. The organization developed strong support from women in the community, established a monitoring system with the aims of stopping the addition of new bottling plants and closing down the existing one. According to one of the participants, "The government only thinks about getting more income from bottled water companies, but they have to prioritize the farmers. With one company sucking out the water now, farmers have had problems obtaining water. If . . . more companies [are added], this will finish off the farmers" (Klaten Online 2008).

Conversion of water into a privatized and saleable commodity is an important threat to the already tenuous access to water that many people in the world have today. This process underlines the fact that limited water access and the health consequences that flow from this circumstance are in no small part products of unequal political economic relations and not merely a result of the unequal global distribution of natural water sources.

HEALTH CARE AND THE SOCIAL WELFARE AGENDA

While some might argue that we can live without health care because it is not a basic necessity for existence, we make the case that, like food and water, health care should be a common good and a basic human right. We use the example of maternal and child health to support this claim.

Maternal and Child Health

Maternal and child health have long been key variables in the assessment of health inequalities between and within nations. Two of the eight Millennium Development Goals (MDGs) for 2015 set forth by the United Nations Millennium Declaration in 2000 focus on the reduction of maternal and child mortality. According to WHO, approximately 358,000 women die each year during pregnancy and childbirth primarily due to hemorrhage, infection, high blood pressure, unsafe abortion, and obstructed labor—all causes that have effective biomedical treatments. But women in many parts of the world do not have access to skilled routine and emergency perinatal care or safe abortion. In 2010, 7.6 million children under five died, and 90 percent of these deaths can be attributed to six conditions: neonatal causes, pneumonia, diarrhea, malaria, measles, and HIV/AIDS, all of which are exacerbated by malnutrition. These conditions are preventable and treatable.

Because maternal and child mortality are primarily caused by preventable or treatable conditions, experts agree that access to basic health care is, in fact, necessary to life. In table 4.1 (on the following page) we compare the United States, with its high-income/low–social agenda system, to other countries with different combinations of these two factors (from high-income/high–social agenda health care systems to low-income/low–social agenda health care systems) on four key indicators of maternal and child health status: (1) infant mortality, (2) under age five child mortality, (3) maternal mortality ratio, and (4) percentage of births attended by a skilled birth attendant (e.g., doctor, nurse, midwife, maternal child health worker meeting minimum training requirements developed by WHO).

Globally, the best health outcomes in terms of infant, child, and maternal mortality are found in societies with a social welfare agenda that includes redistribution of resources and social safety nets (Birn et al. 2009). Examples in the developed world include Sweden, Denmark, Norway, and the United Kingdom, all of which have very low rates on the mortality measures and a high percentage of deliveries with a skilled attendant. Surprisingly, however, many less developed countries that have chosen a social welfare agenda (and have not been forced by SAPs to abandon it) have achieved levels of health that are comparable to those of the highly industrialized wealthy nations. Examples include Costa Rica, Cuba, Sri Lanka, and Uruguay, which also have admirably low maternal and child mortality rates and iden-

Table 4.1 Infant, Child, and Maternal Mortality Indicators for Selected Countries.*

Country	Infant Mortality[1] per 1,000 Live Births	Under-5 Mortality[2] per 1,000	Maternal Mortality Ratio[3] per 100,000 Live Births	Skilled Birth Attendant Percent
Developed Countries with Social Welfare Agenda				
Denmark	3	4	12	97.8%
Norway	3	3	7	99.1%
Sweden	2	3	4	N/A
United Kingdom	5	5	12	99.0%
United States—Limited Social Welfare Agenda				
United States	7	8	21	99.3%
Less Developed Countries with Social Welfare Agenda				
Costa Rica	9	10	40	95.3%
Cuba	5	6	73	99.9%
Sri Lanka	14	17	35	98.6%
Uruguay	9	11	29	99.7%
Least Developed Countries with Limited Social Welfare Agenda				
Afghanistan	103	149	460	34.3%
Bangladesh	38	48	240	26.5%
Haiti	70	165	350	26.1%
Kenya	55	85	360	43.8%
Mali	99	178	540	49.0%

* Adapted from WHO Child Health Indicators, Maternal Health Indicators
[1] Deaths to children under 1 year of age.
[2] Deaths to children age 1 up to their fifth birthday.
[3] Deaths to women while pregnant or within 42 days of termination of pregnancy from any cause related to or aggravated by the pregnancy or its management but not from accidental or incidental causes.

tical proportions of births attended by skilled practitioners as the high-income countries. The United States falls between these two groups. Countries with the highest rates are the least developed and have little in the way of health care services outside of major cities and minimal social safety nets. These countries include Afghanistan, Bangladesh, Haiti, Kenya, and Mali. Maternal and child mortality rates are very high in all these countries.

Infant mortality rates are lowest in the most developed nations, intermediate in less developed countries with high social agendas, and highest in the least developed countries. The range in infant mortality rates globally is wide, from two per 1,000 births in several Scandinavian countries to 112 in the Democratic Republic of the Congo. In comparison, the rates achieved in all but the least developed countries in table 4.1 are remarkably low. Infant mortality (after the neonatal period, the first 38 days of life, when death is due more to congenital conditions that are incompatible with life) is greatly affected by socioeconomic status and living conditions as well as access to health care and breastfeeding.

Like infant mortality, child mortality rates are lowest in the most developed countries, ranging from two per 100,000 in Finland, Iceland, and Japan as contrasted with 180 in an underdeveloped country like Somalia. Deaths in this age group are often related to infectious diseases and their interaction with malnutrition, which are largely preventable conditions, again reflecting socioeconomic status, living conditions, and access to immunizations and basic health services. While child mortality rates have decreased since the 1960s due to programs targeted to improve child health, many of the gains have been halted or reversed, especially in Africa where HIV/AIDS, famine, war, and complex humanitarian emergencies have decimated the social infrastructure.

Maternal mortality is also affected by socioeconomic status and living conditions, but more prominently by access to prenatal care, safe labor and delivery with a skilled birth attendant, and access to postpartum care. Maternal mortality ratios by WHO regions range from 20 in Europe (lowest is two in Estonia) to a high of 480 in sub-Saharan Africa (highest is 1,100 in Chad). Ninety-nine percent of maternal deaths occur in the less developed countries. More than half are in sub-Saharan Africa, and nearly a third are in South Asia (WHO 2012). The percentages of women attended by a skilled birth attendant by WHO region (Europe, Americas, Eastern Mediterranean, Africa, Southeast Asia, and the Western Pacific) range from 98 percent in Europe to 48 percent in Africa. The association between access to a trained birth attendant and health is especially apparent for maternal mortality.

In an accessibly written book, former Peace Corps volunteer Kris Holloway (2007) chronicles her two-year experience assisting Monique, a trained midwife and community health worker in rural Mali, and provides an up-close-and-personal understanding of the toll of poverty and lack of health care on women and children. Monique faces numerous challenges in her quest to provide maternal and child health care to her community. Her clinic/birthing center is deteriorating. Water must be hauled from the village well that is far from the clinic. There is no electricity. She rarely has the basic medicine and equipment she needs to attend to births and sick children. Infectious disease, diarrhea, and malnutrition are rampant among the children in the community, and child mortality is high. Women have many births, draining them of vitality. Monique is overworked, and her husband controls both the motorbike she needs for her work and her paycheck, leaving her without transportation, as well as financial and social support. Yet, Monique and Kris persist, teaching women about the importance of clean water and prevention of childhood infectious diseases, appropriate weaning foods, and the value of prenatal care and postpartum rest, birth control, and child spacing. There are many small gains, but the large political, social, and economic challenges—little power for women in the patriarchal society, lack of a transportation system and basic resources, and, finally, civil war—overwhelm them.

Health Care as a Human Right

In the United States, we are used to thinking of health care as a commodity, but the reality is that we have a very mixed private/public system. We pay for health care in a number of ways—out-of-pocket expenditures, through private health insurance purchased individually or as part of an employer benefit program to which we contribute, or through our taxes for programs for the military, the elderly, and the indigent.

The military has socialized medicine paid for by federal tax dollars for its active duty personnel, their families, and retirees until age 65. Medicare is a kind of national health insurance for Americans age 65 and older, paid for largely by federal tax dollars. Those without insurance may be able to get state and federal subsidized insurance (Medicaid) if they are poor enough. Those who can't afford to pay privately but don't qualify as poor enough for Medicaid must rely on charity (e.g., free clinics, emergency rooms, etc.).

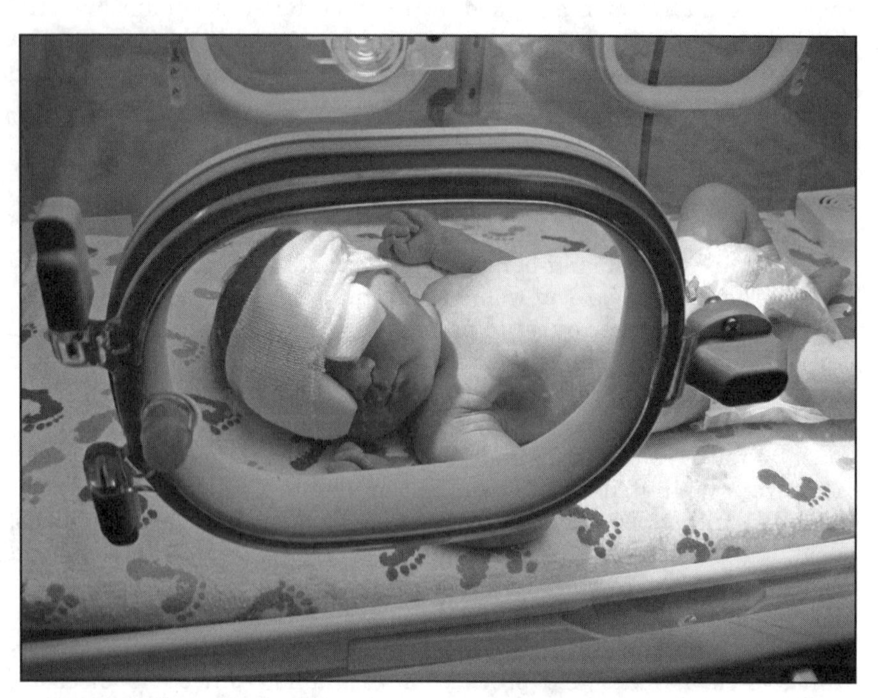

Incubator use and modern high-tech reproductive health in developed countries. (Pamela Erickson)

There are 49.9 million uninsured Americans, 16.3 percent of the population (US Census Bureau 2011). Many of the uninsured are children (eight million) and women of reproductive age. This probably accounts for why infant, child, and maternal mortality rates in the United States are higher than those of European nations with strong social welfare agendas in which all women and children have access to health care, education, housing, and food

In chapter 1 we discussed the history of global health efforts and suggested that the main problem in global health today is that there is no system, no participatory governing body, and no health care agenda or philosophy on which all interested parties agree. Indeed, there are opposing agendas. Recall that today, global financial institutions, large corporate and private philanthropic organizations, and the medical-pharmaceutical industrial complex, rather than participatory international organizations like WHO, are setting the agenda for global health. The financial institutions have imposed neoliberal economic policies—free trade, market economy, privatization of health care and resources—on poor countries that need loans or cannot repay their debts. These policies have destroyed the public health care systems in many developing countries and forced many to abandon socialized medical systems and the promise of primary health care for all. Countering this neoliberal agenda and its disastrous impact on the health of the global poor is a disorganized, relatively powerless group of organizations (e.g., WHO, United Nations), nations, and individuals that champion a more socially responsible agenda for global health that is framed from a human rights perspective. We join the latter group that claims that food, water, and primary health care are basic human rights that governments must provide for their citizens.

CONCLUSION

Human beings cannot live much more than two to ten days, depending on the climate, without drinking water. At the most, we can live perhaps 45–60 days without food if we have water. Both food and water are vital for life. We discussed the problems inherent in transforming basic human needs for food and water into commodities to be bought and sold in an open market and the process by which food and water have been transformed from collective resources that are shared among all human beings to commodities that are purchased by those who can afford them. We have described the misery and ill health that commoditization of food and water has caused globally, contributing significantly to the growing health disparities between rich and poor individuals, nations, and world regions. Health inequalities in maternal and child mortality are particularly upsetting because they are largely preventable by access to clean water and sufficient food or treatable by modern biomedicine. It is for this reason that we argue that basic health care is a human right, not a commodity to be bought and sold.

Note

[1] BMI is calculated by dividing a person's body weight by the square of his or her height and multiplying the answer by 703.

Chapter Five

Our Changing World

The global health community faces a number of significant challenges when seeking to build a global health initiative to effect significant measurable improvements in the health and well-being of the world's populations. First, such an initiative must be based on a global network of transnational health institutions, resources, workers, and activists that agree on the issues. Beyond this, however, there are other challenges in our new global world that are highly political and often controversial and that have generated public awareness and concern. We address five of these challenges in this chapter: (1) the growing frequency of complex humanitarian emergencies that threaten the ability of global health workers to act swiftly and effectively to prevent loss of life, suffering, and destruction of health-related infrastructure; (2) **armed combat** that extends the battlefield to civilian populations intentionally or unintentionally; (3) anthropogenic biohazard threats due to failures of corporate production and transport systems and as a war tactic; (4) the mounting number of **refugee and otherwise displaced populations**—victims especially of war but of environmental and climate disasters as well; and (5) the **global tobacco and alcohol epidemics**.

COMPLEX HUMANITARIAN EMERGENCIES

An increasingly common threat to global health in the contemporary world, a **complex humanitarian emergency (CHE)** is defined as a humanitarian crisis in a country, region, or multiple regions in which there is a total or extensive breakdown of authority and order resulting from internal or external conflict, which requires an international response beyond the mandate or capacity of any single existing program (Burkle 1999). CHE situations are becoming more common despite efforts to curtail their occurrence. In such emergencies, there is a health-threatening convergence of several factors including violent conflict, mass forced migration, destruction of infrastructure, political-economic state collapse, and the breakdown of community-level and national social structures such as health care services. CHEs are characterized by the disruption of medical supplies, health service facilities, disease surveillance and prevention programs (such as childhood inoculation), and health education efforts. Disruption of food production and distribution systems adds to the health risks. Also at risk are health care providers, who may be targeted for harm in conflict situations. Damage to the health of civilians and health care systems is often a collateral effect of military conflict but may be the objective as a means of weakening an enemy's will and ability to fight. In these instances, attacks on health care systems, facilities, and providers are used as a weapon of war. Such events cause more death, disease, and disability than all other types of disasters combined (Brennan and Nandy 2001). During complex humanitarian emergencies, mortality rates increase dramatically.

CHEs require organized, focused, and multifaceted global health responses delivered within short time frames, under challenging conditions of physical accessibility, social conflict, and unfavorable climate. An example of this kind of complex emergency was the Liberian civil war of 1990–1997. During this prolonged brutal conflict, involving at least six different military factions, approximately 150,000 civilians were massacred, as many as 700,000 civilians were forcibly displaced to neighboring nations, and 90 percent of the health care infrastructure was destroyed or degraded. In 1994, one of Liberia's last remaining hospitals was destroyed, and hundreds of its staff and displaced persons who were seeking shelter there were slaughtered (Schowengerdt et al. 1998). During the conflict, emergency efforts frequently had to be halted because of renewed conflict.

The Liberian crisis provided the global health community with a number of important lessons. First, it affirmed the need for establishing a permanent emergency intervention program in the global health community. Second, the crisis underlined the value of gaining on-the-ground (e.g., ethnographic) understanding of the nature of a conflict—its background, history, and the different forms of violence it generates, all of which influence the nature of health outcomes. Third, this case suggested the importance of developing flexible emergency response capacity, because complex emergencies are not always static; rather, they can remain in long-term flux between periods of peak crisis when humanitarian intervention is impossible and periods of greater stability conducive to recovery and reconstruction activities. Finally, the Liberian civil war revealed why the term *complex humanitarian emergency* is an accurate label for such events. The conflict was a moving target with unexpected twists and turns, resulting in enormous challenges to those seeking to protect civilians and address food, housing, and medical needs during this pressing humanitarian crisis.

One approach for assessing the public health impact of CHEs like the civil war in Liberia is the **mortality survey**, the calculation of crude death rates suffered by a population during an emergency. *Crude death rates* are defined as deaths per 10,000 population per day and deaths of those under five years of age per 10,000 population per day. These data are compiled in the Complex Emergency Database (CE-DAT), which is accessible online at: http://www.cedat.org/. CE-DAT is a global initiative managed by the Centre for Research on the Epidemiology of Disasters (CRED) based at the School of Public Health of the Université Catholique de Louvain in Brussels, Belgium. The program was launched in 2003 to assemble, standardize, and monitor data on the health status of populations affected by CHEs and to use this information to assess needs, develop evidence-based policy on conflict prevention, and inform effective response initiatives. By

Medical evacuation from Tuvalu. (Julie Park)

2011, the CE-DAT contained 2,400 epidemiological surveys conducted in 51 countries. Information on nutrition and mortality are emphasized in the database. These two measures provide a measure of the overall welfare of a population. While mortality rates are the ultimate indicator of population well-being, nutrition and other health status data comprise the starting point for prevention and health programs.

The development of CE-DAT responded to a 2003 meeting held in Stockholm, Sweden, of government and multilateral donor organizations, several UN institutions, the International Red Cross and Red Crescent Movement, and other organizations involved in international humanitarian efforts. The goals of the meeting were to review the past efforts and achievements of the humanitarian community and to define a new paradigm to guide decision making and priority setting among donor organizations. One of the principles adopted at the meeting was that the allocation of humanitarian funding and other aid should be proportional to the identified level of need based on sound needs assessment. In other words, research is a critical element in humanitarian aid.

CRED seeks to stimulate a global discussion of the effectiveness of humanitarian responses to global emergencies. In 2010, CE-DAT publicized a study showing that almost 80 percent of the estimated 300,000 conflict-related deaths recorded in the Darfur region of Sudan were caused by infections—especially diarrheal disease among children—rather than the direct result of violence. CE-DAT used this finding to show the grave consequence of the expulsion of aid workers from Sudan by the country's president, Omar Hassan al-Bashir, and to emphasize the need to implement interventions targeted at infectious diseases.

In the Darfur study, data on when and how people died and the nutritional status of children were collected from a sample of families among the 2.7 million refugees from Darfur living in refugee camps. Researchers used a **cluster sampling method** to select participants for surveys. Cluster sampling involves: (1) identifying population units (e.g., villages, districts, town sections) and estimating their populations, which are grouped into clusters based on geographic location; (2) randomly selecting a predetermined number of clusters for study; (3) within each cluster, randomly selecting a predetermined number of households or similar units; and (4) weighing and measuring all children between the ages of six months and 59 months in each household selected for inclusion.

The results allow estimations of mortality and the impact of the CHE on child nutrition. The latter data are compared to a reference population of normally fed children. This allows researchers to identify children who are **wasted** (i.e., suffering from acute malnutrition that produces deficits in weight-for-height measurements), **stunted** (chronically malnourished, producing deficits in height-for-age measurements), and **underweight** (acutely and chronically malnourished, producing deficits in weight-for-age measurements). Each child is examined for the presence of a condition known as *bilateral pitting edema*, which is a sign of *kwashiorkor*, a form of severe malnutrition. The percentage of malnourished children in the sample is then presented in terms of "Global Acute Malnutrition" (GAM), "Global Chronic Malnutrition" (GCM) or "Global Underweight" (GU). These measures reflect recent nutritional status and are used as a proxy for the overall health of a population. For example, GAM rates above 15 percent in a population are seen as critical. While physically, methodologically (e.g., exact ages are often not known), and emotionally difficult work, collection and analysis of data like these are critical to global responses to CHEs.

In 2011 CE-DAT published an assessment of CHEs in eight African nations: Chad, Democratic Republic of the Congo, Ethiopia, Kenya, Niger, Sudan, Somalia, and Uganda (Centre for Research on the Epidemiology of Disasters 2011). One of the key findings of this study was that based on "Surveys included in the CE-DAT database . . . health and nutrition status of the populations affected by complex emergencies . . . has improved during the last ten years [2000–2009]" (12). This finding suggests that we are learning, if slowly from the standpoint of impacted populations, how to best respond to complex emergencies.

WAR AND GENOCIDE

The violent conflicts in Liberia and the Darfur region of Sudan underline the substantial impact of wars on contemporary global health while affirming the contemporary effort to define war as a central public health issue (Levy and Sidel 2008). This movement is driven by the fact that the twentieth century—during which both the Liberia and Sudan conflicts began—was "the bloodiest [century] in human history" (Garfield 2008:25), with two costly "world wars" that together caused at least 80 million deaths as well as an untold number of injuries and widespread suffering. Since the conclusion of World War II, there have been 160 wars around the world, with at least 25 million people killed, the majority of them civilians (Levy and Sidel 2008). But the immediate casualties of war comprise only the tip of the iceberg of war-related damage to global human well-being (Pedersen 2009).

A Sri Lankan woman who lived through the ravages of war told anthropologist Carolyn Nordstrom, a pioneer of war-zone **ethnography**, about the suffering of war-displaced women routinely robbed by the police of their few worldly possessions and admonished her, "Tell the truth of war and what happens to people like these women who stand on the thin line of survival" (2004:8). Using the holistic and ethnographically informed perspective of medical anthropology, it is evident that the ravages of war are multiple, diverse, and prolonged over many years or even decades, and they affect various sectors of society differently (Singer and Hodge 2010). Researchers from several disciplines have documented many of the "other costs" of war beyond immediate loss of life and wounded combatants. Most notable among these are civilian noncombatant deaths and injuries. During the twentieth century, there were approximately 45 million military deaths and 62 million civilian war-related deaths (Sivard 1996). Nordstrom (1997) studied the Mozambican Civil War (1975–1994) during which almost a million people, mostly noncombatants, died (many from starvation); millions became refugees; and brutalities were routinely committed against civilians, including rape.

At particular risk in modern wars are children. In a study of 22 children who were caught in various wars in Central America and who subsequently fled to the US, Locke, et al. (1996) found that 18 suffered from chronic health and mental health problems. In many cases, caretakers were not aware of the problems because the children hid them from adults. As Giroux (2009) stresses, "Children no longer serve as an ethical referent against barbarism, they simply become collateral damage, while a ghastly and inhuman act is justified under the pretense of historical necessity and 'surgical strikes.'"

Another issue is the continued health care needs of those who have been wounded and remain in need long after a war has ended. Since the US war in Vietnam, for example, improvements in body armor have significantly increased the likelihood of surviving severe war wounds. Seventy-five percent of American soldiers who suffered traumatic brain injury (TBI) in Vietnam died, but there was a threefold reduction in mortality from TBI in the US wars in Iraq and Afghanistan despite the frequency of explosion injuries in these two wars. Ongoing morbidities, including speech deficits, loss of cognitive skills, depression, and anxiety, are common among brain injury survivors.

Poisoning and other degradation of the environment are other enduring consequences of war. Minefields, including an estimated 70 million to 100 million antipersonnel explosives that are still active and in place in over 75 countries worldwide, continue to cause injury and death to civilians, especially children, long after a war's end. Environmental damage is also caused by the intentional release of forces in nature, such as bombing a dam or causing a forest fire. The diverse ways that war thoroughly damages environments are compounded by interaction with other anthropogenic impacts on the environment, from the use of fossil fuels to the buildup of greenhouse gases to industrial air, water, and land pollution. Interactions that exacerbate environmental degradation and disruption (e.g., global warming) are beginning to have significant impact on human health (Baer 2010).

Another global health consequence of war is the facilitation of epidemics. For example, while smallpox had been almost wiped out in Bangladesh prior to its war of independence with Pakistan in 1971–1972, the disease quickly began spreading anew during the war, resulting in over 18,000 deaths. Similarly, Uganda had achieved widespread immunization of children prior to its civil war, but coverage rapidly declined to less than 10 percent of eligible children for TB and less than 5 percent for diphtheria, pertussis, tetanus, and poliomyelitis (Machel 1996).

While war continues to spread diseases, the relationship between these two primary causes of human mortality has been in transition. In the past, disease provided a degree of constraint on war to the extent that it weakened the fighting capacity of armies. Today, soldiers are protected from most infectious diseases, keeping them fit to fight (Coker 2004). However, with the spread of modern biological warfare, disease is not only a consequence of war but also potentially a more deadly weapon in the war arsenal.

Wars can leave an enduring mark on the quality of health care systems and other infrastructure. The United Nations, for example, found that by the end of the Indochina wars, in 1991, Cambodia had only 30 doctors left (Machel 1996). As a result of the US-funded Contra War against the Sandinista government in Nicaragua (1982–1987), almost a quarter of the country's health centers were partially or fully destroyed or forced to close because of frequent attacks by the right-wing Contras. For poor countries, the road back from war can be long with health consequences from malnutrition to reproductive health problems resulting from damaged transportation and production and limited health services.

As this list, incomplete as it is, suggests, the wounds of war are multiple and run deep. Sometimes they fester and become the emotional force fueling future wars, as well as more immediate health consequences, such as domestic violence, suicide, posttraumatic stress syndrome, and similar long-term hidden costs of war. Assisting countries and people in healing the physical and psychological wounds of war is now an imperative arena of work in global health.

BIOHAZARDS SINCE 9/11

In our post-9/11 world, public health discourse has been inundated with a host of new "threat words," words that label emergent dangers to human and planetary health and well-being, such as *biohazards*. Biohazards are infectious agents or hazardous biological materials that present a risk or potential risk to the health of humans, animals, or the environment. The risk of biohazards can be direct through infection (e.g., anthrax) or indirect through damage to the environment. Biohazardous materials include certain types of recombinant DNA, organisms and viruses infectious to humans, animals, or plants, and biologically active agents (e.g., toxins, allergens, venoms) that can cause disease in living organisms or cause significant impact on the environment or community.

The threat of biohazards did not begin on September 11, 2001. Forty years earlier, Rachel Carson published *Silent Spring*, a book that generated public awareness of the significant biothreat posed by pesticides like DDT (dichlorodiphenyltrichloroethane). Because this organochlorine insecticide builds up in animal and human bodies, with concentrations increasing the higher a species is in the food chain, it has the potential to cause significant health damage and disease (e.g., cancers, diabetes, fetal damage) and the loss of biodiversity as species disappear (e.g., birds, because their eggs are made fragile by the chemical). Banning DDT did not eliminate the biohazardous threat of pesticides, as DDT has been replaced by other agrochemicals, some of which are far more toxic.

In 1997, a massive public health initiative directed by WHO culminated in the eradication of all known smallpox viruses from the world, except for samples saved in laboratories in Russia and the US ostensibly for research purposes. As a result, the United States stopped giving smallpox vaccinations in 1972. In 1980, WHO recommended that all countries stop vaccinating for smallpox. The fate of the last remaining smallpox pathogens currently is on the agenda of WHO, which is considering whether or not to push for their destruction. Some countries want to destroy the smallpox strains so they can never be accidentally released or used as a bioweapon, creating a deadly biohazard. The US government, however, wants to keep its samples, arguing they are still needed to develop new therapies and vaccines even though the potential for a smallpox accident in the laboratory is real.

CDC categorizes diseases into four levels of biohazard:

- *Biohazard Level 1* indicates use of low-level precautions against the biohazardous materials, usually involving the mandated use of gloves and facial protection. In a laboratory, Level 1 materials are left in the open.
- *Biohazard Level 2* involves bacteria and viruses that cause only mild disease in humans, or pathogens that are difficult to contract via aerosol in a laboratory setting, such as hepatitis or HIV. Research involving these pathogens is allowed in a prepared facility with some restrictive guidelines.
- *Biohazard Level 3* involves bacteria and viruses that can cause severe to fatal disease in humans, but for which vaccines or other treatments already exist, such as West Nile virus, SARS virus, and smallpox.

- *Biohazard Level 4* involves viruses and bacteria that cause severe to fatal disease in humans, and for which vaccines or other treatments are not available, such as Bolivian and Argentine hemorrhagic fevers. Very stringent rules guide the handling of these pathogens to ensure they do not infect laboratory workers or escape to the outside world.

Yet, accidents happen. In July 2009, a container with vials of swine flu virus exploded on a Swiss Intercity train during a peak passenger time, exposing 61 people to a potentially lethal virus. The container was sent from a WHO and Baxter Corporation–affiliated laboratory in Mexico City and was destined for the National Influenza Laboratory of Switzerland in Geneva. The container may have been improperly packaged; the dry ice meant to cool the vials was packed in the wrong part of the container and melted, resulting in an explosion in the train compartment.

Similarly, on January 6, 2005, two freight trains collided in Graniteville, South Carolina. One of the trains included a number of chlorine tanker cars, which were damaged in the crash. Chlorine is a highly volatile, inorganic gas that acts as a direct cellular toxin. The crash led to the immediate release of more than 11,000 gallons of chlorine into the local environment, resulting in nine fatalities. Also, more than 500 people sought medical care at nearby hospitals and physicians' offices, and 69 people, primarily with respiratory complaints, were admitted to area hospitals. Local businesses and schools had to be closed, and more than 5,000 residents within a one-mile radius of the incident site were evacuated.

Biohazards develop in other ways as well. During floods or catastrophic explosions, biohazards can become significant threats. Sewage backups can occur during severe rainstorms and floods. Sewage contains bacteria and viruses that can cause gastrointestinal distress, skin rashes, and other infections. Commercial and residential buildings that get flooded during storms may contain hazardous chemicals like solvents, pesticides, and fertilizers. For example, dry-cleaning operations use chemicals such as perchloroethylene and petroleum hydrocarbon, two highly toxic substances. During flooding, dangerous chemicals can be carried away by fast-moving flood waters and contaminate drinking water sources.

Oil spills are another significant biohazard. While the chemical composition of crude oil can vary tremendously by region of the world, crude oil generally consists of a complex combination of hydrocarbons and other chemicals. As seen in the 2010 Gulf Oil spill, oil spills present a significant threat to human health and the health of the environments they inhabit. One of the dangers of oil spills in the ocean is that the oil can appear to be completely dissolved, unnoticeable in the water. Chemical testing, however, shows that toxic levels of oil can exist in seemingly clear water. There is growing suspicion that the massive Gulf Oil spill is not over and that it has fundamentally changed the ocean, with potentially serious consequences for human health (Bond 2011).

Although the Gulf Oil spill was the largest in US history, it is not a unique event. In July 2011, for example, oil burst through a 12-inch ExxonMobil pipeline located at the bottom of the Yellowstone River in Montana, spewing 42 thousand gallons of crude oil into the river. In July of the previous year, a spill from a rupture in the Enbridge Energy pipeline in Michigan leaked in excess of one million gallons of oil into Talmadge Creek, which flows into the Kalamazoo River.

A particularly notable spill occurred in May 2010 when a ruptured ExxonMobil pipeline in Nigeria poured more than a million gallons into the Niger Delta. It was more than seven days before the leak was stopped. The delta is home to about 20 million people from 40 different ethnic groups; its waters consist of coastal barrier islands, mangrove swamp forests, freshwater swamps, lowland rain forests, and wildlife. The delta was once an extremely well-endowed ecosystem, containing the highest concentrations of biodiversity in West Africa. Over the past 50 years, however, Nigeria and its delta have been caught in an intertwined political ecological crisis of pollution and corruption.

The human rights group, Amnesty International, estimates that more than nine million barrels of oil have been spilled in the delta in recent years, an amount nearly double that which leaked into the Gulf of Mexico. The United Nations recorded over 6,800 oil spills from 1976 to 2001 in the delta (Parker 2009). The delta's oil field consists of over 606 wells, making Nigeria the sixth largest oil producer in the world. Its networks of oil field piping are highly prone to spills and leaks, mostly due to aging, extensive corrosion, and poor maintenance. The World Wildlife Fund calls the delta "one of the most polluted places on the face of the earth" (Thill 2008). According to Williams Mkpa, a community leader in Ibeno, Nigeria, "Oil companies do not value our life; they want us to all die. In the past two years, we have experienced 10 oil spills and fishermen can no longer sustain their families. It is not tolerable" (quoted in Vidal 2010).

While many studies have focused on acute physical and psychological effects of crude oil exposure on human physical health, very few have examined the long-term repercussions. A review of the tanker spill studies to date (Aguilera et al. 2010) suggests the need for **biomonitoring** human populations exposed to spilled oil, especially those involved in cleanup operations. Assessment of people involved in the cleanup of oil spilled off the coast of France in 1999 (*Erika* tanker), found that 8 percent experienced some type of wound and 53 percent some health problem (i.e., 30% lumbar pain, 22% migraine, 16% dermatitis). The duration of their involvement in cleanup work was identified as a critical risk factor.

There are many other kinds of biohazards besides oil spills. On December 3, 1984, for example, there was a massive explosion at the Union Carbide Corporation pesticide plant in Bhopal, India. Bhopal, with a population of 900,000 people, was largely an impoverished shanty town that had grown up just outside of the plant boundary. The explosion released over 25 tons of lethal gases, immediately killing more than 3,000 people and injuring 200,000 others, many of whom were blinded. Eventually, as many as 20,000 people died as a result of the explosion. The accident followed a series of cost-cutting measures that left the safety system designed to contain leaks inoperative, including the public warning siren. In its public statement on the tragedy, Union Carbide, which since 2001 has been a subsidiary of the Dow Chemical Company, downplayed its role and responsibility by placing the blame on its Indian partners.

Biohazards are created in a number of ways including industrial accidents combined with inadequate prevention policies and safety enforcement, insufficient regulation of dangerous industries, war and conflict, storms and violent weather, the intentional discard of medical waste and other biodumping, and the transportation of hazardous materials. The collapse of the World Trade Center towers, for example, released dioxins, PCBs, benzene, lead, and chromium into the air and soil. A study of rescue workers at the site by the CDC (2002) found that 60 percent suffered lower respiratory problems, 74 percent suffered upper respiratory problems, 46 percent had nasal mucosal inflammation, and 33 percent had abnormal pulmonary function findings. A follow-up examination of 182 pregnant women who were either inside or near the World Trade Center on 9/11 found a twofold increase in small-for-gestational-age infants (Landrigan et al. 2004).

Collectively, biohazard events have become an increasing concern of global public health efforts, as their frequency has increased and their impact on human populations has grown. Consequently, the emphasis on prevention and response planning, prevention policies, the development and dissemination of guidelines, and the preparation of rescue initiatives has been augmented. Evaluations of these efforts are far from adequate. Overall, the long-term health impacts of biohazard events remain an understudied topic.

THE REFUGEE CRISIS

Complex emergencies, war, and environmental disasters are producing a growing number of refugees in the world. This is a mounting global health concern since refugees inevitably have poorer health than do settled populations. The 2009 report of the United Nations

Refugee Agency (Office of the United Nations High Commissioner for Refugees 2009) indicated that there are over 40 million people in the world who have been uprooted from their homes by conflict and persecution. Eighty percent of these displaced individuals live in developing nations, and most are internally displaced persons (living within their own country but away from their traditional home area). Among those who are forced to flee their country, most move to a country neighboring their own. Many individuals have been refugees for years with no likelihood of repatriation on the horizon. The UN also reports that in 2010 there were more than 15,500 unaccompanied or separated children, mainly from Afghanistan and Somalia, among the world's refugee population. Overall, the three major source countries for refugees through the end of 2010 were Afghanistan, Iraq, and Somalia (Office of the United Nations High Commissioner for Refugees 2010).

In addition to conflict and persecution, environmental disasters produce refugee populations. The Inter-Agency Standing Committee (2008) estimates that by 2050 the number of people who will be forced to move from their homes as a result of climate change and environmental degradation is between 25 million and one billion. The Global Governance Project, a joint research program sponsored by 11 European research institutes, concluded that "climate change threatens to cause the largest refugee crisis in human history" (Biermann and Boas 2007:ii). Mahe Noor, a 25-year-old woman who lived with her husband and children in a rural area of southern Bangladesh, was forced to flee when Cyclone Sidr destroyed their home and small market in 2007 (Kakissis 2010). Homeless and jobless, the family joined the throngs of people moving into the capital city of Dhaka, believing the move would be temporary. Several years have gone by and they are still living there in a slum. They were able to find work—Mahe at a garment factory and her husband at a roadside tea stall—but they make so little money none can be saved to allow them to move back home. They feel trapped and frustrated. Making matters worse, river erosion and shrinking economic opportunities in their home village push more people into the capital.

Four areas of the world, Asia, Africa, Latin America, and the small islands of Oceania have the largest populations at risk of becoming climate refugees. Asian nations are vulnerable because many have highly populated, low-lying coastal areas and are vulnerable to cyclones. It is estimated that if average temperatures rise two to three degrees, as many as 800 million people in southern Asia, especially those living in Bangladesh, will be at high risk for flooding that will force them to flee their homes. By contrast, African nations are vulnerable to the regional droughts that will be caused by global warming. As sudden climate events like hurricanes and flooding reveal, every person on the planet is a potential environmental refugee, although some have far more resources to respond to this kind of crisis than others.

The issue of global refugees is complicated by international legal definitions, which are defended by organizations committed to ensuring aid for particular kinds of refugees, such as victims of persecution. Under the 1951 Refugee Convention (part of the Geneva Convention), a refugee is defined as a person who, because of a well-founded fear of persecution for reasons of race, religion, nationality, membership in a social group, holding particular political views, or being the subject of aggression and conflict, must flee his or her country of usual residence. In international law, an individual who moves because of a natural or anthropogenic environmental disaster, a group increasingly referred to informally as a "climate or environmental refugees," officially is not counted as being a refugee. Other labels, such as internally displaced persons and stateless persons (individuals who are not accepted as citizens in any country) are also part of the international legal lexicon (Inter-Agency Standing Committee 2008).

From a global health standpoint, the causes of displacement are primarily only of relevance as they impact health consequences—war victims and drought victims may have quite different needs—or as they facilitate or restrict the provision of humanitarian and medical aid. Calls for the development of international agreements about responding to the needs of climate and environmental refugees are on the rise, as this group in the future will likely outnumber all other groups who have been displaced. While some in the global governance and global health communities have called for extending the Geneva Convention agreements to cover climate and environmental refugees, others believe a new international legal agreement is needed that is tailored to the needs of this population. Continued climate change and other environmental degradation will force decisions on this matter within coming years. Whichever approach is taken, the health needs of refugees of all kinds warrant intensified examination.

Mortality rates in refugee populations have been found to be extremely high, up to 60 times expected levels, especially during the acute phase immediately after dislocation. Displaced populations in northern Ethiopia (in 1985) and southern Sudan (in 1988), involving poor populations being forced to move to equally poor new locations, were found to suffer extraordinary mortality rates. Although high rates were found in all age groups, excess mortality was the greatest in 1–14-year-olds, with measles, diarrheal diseases, acute respiratory tract infections, and malaria being primary immediate causes. Progression of infectious diseases among refugees often is fueled by protein-energy and micronutrient deficiencies caused by dislocation (Toole and Waldman 1990).

As this discussion suggests, the health needs of refugees are multiple, and often are greater and more diverse than the preparation efforts of international responses. Resettlement efforts often do not lead to improved conditions for resettlers. Anthropologist Chris de Wet

(2006) argues this is a consequence both of inadequate planning, resources, and knowledge among resettlement authorities and of the failure of top-down approaches to involve resettlers in planning and implementation decision making.

Anthropologists have attempted to improve resettlement efforts by advocating participatory approaches and by looking at resettlement as a staged process with different needs at different points in time. The concerns of the second generation that comes of age in the new settlement may be far different than the day-to-day survival focus of the first generation (Scudder and Colson 1982). Michael Cernea and Christopher McDowell (2000) differentiated the multiple kinds of risk encountered in and after resettlement. Their study reflected **experience-near** knowledge born of on-the-ground ethnographic work in refugee and resettlement settings that led to a better understanding of the complexities of resettlement and the need for workable planning models (Oliver-Smith 2009).

THE TOBACCO AND ALCOHOL EPIDEMICS

The term "drug" has been defined in various ways. In this book, we refer to any chemical compound that when ingested in some fashion produces a change in the body's functional state, especially a psychotropic change involving an altering of the mind or mental condition of the consumer. While considerable media and government attention focuses on reporting and controlling illegal drugs (e.g., marijuana, heroin, cocaine), most health impacts of drug use globally are the result of consuming legal drugs like tobacco and alcohol, as well as diverted and misused pharmaceutical drugs. According to the United Nations Office of Drugs and Crime (2006), drugs of all kinds are involved in almost 15 percent of yearly deaths worldwide. WHO estimates there are under 200 million illicit drug users compared to 1.3 billion tobacco smokers and two billion alcohol consumers (and, of course, considerable overlap because of multiple-drug users). The disease burden caused by the various classes of drugs varies by WHO world region, with alcohol and tobacco having the largest negative impact in Europe and the lowest in the Eastern Mediterranean. Adverse health impacts of alcohol are also quite high comparatively in the Americas and the Western Pacific. Illicit drugs have their highest health consequences in the Americas.

In an effort to address the significant global health issues associated with tobacco and alcohol consumption, global health must confront powerful transnational corporations that gain enormous wealth from marketing and selling killer commodities (Singer and Baer 2009). These corporations are engaged in a reversal of the War on Drugs;

instead they fight a marketing, promotional, and lobbying war "for" drugs. In this war, transnational corporations can muster enormous financial and other resources that successfully undermine the capacity of less developed nations and weak or corrupt national governments to control the flow of harmful corporate commodities. Through internal lending institutions, transnational corporations promote neoliberal global trade policies that reduce trade barriers like tariffs, increase market access, and undermine domestic regulations on tobacco and alcohol access. Global health advocates, as a result, must be aware of the inherent contradictions between public health and free trade and seek to block the inclusion of alcohol and tobacco products in international trade agreements and commercial treaties (Zeigler 2006).

Tobacco and Disease

Tobacco is consumed in various ways, primarily by smoking, but also as snuff or by chewing. Whatever the method, the most powerful force driving continued consumption following initial use is addiction. Nicotine is a natural ingredient of tobacco, is one of 4,000 chemicals in this plant product, and is very addictive. Nicotine is also an ingredient that is heavily manipulated and enhanced by tobacco manufacturers. Cigarettes, for example, are treated with ammonia to produce high doses of freebase nicotine and are designed to produce smoke particles of small and uniform size that carry the nicotine deep into the respiratory system.

Tobacco manufacturing and sales is a big business globally. Philip Morris International, for example, has 50 tobacco products factories in countries around the world and sells its products in over 160 national markets. As Bill Moyers (2002), host of the *NOW* program on PBS, noted, "By Big Tobacco, we mean companies so huge, their revenues dwarf the gross national product of some countries; companies so powerful they can become a law unto themselves." Manufacturers of tobacco products spend billions of dollars yearly to promote tobacco consumption internationally. This effort is quite productive with rates of smoking increasing in many low- and middle-income countries even as rates in some higher-income countries are decreasing as a result of decades-long public health interventions. As a result, WHO (2011) states the "tobacco epidemic is one of the biggest public health threats the world has ever faced."

WHO reports that 100 million people died as a result of using tobacco during the twentieth century and that tobacco consumption is the second-leading cause of mortality in the world, causing five million deaths annually. Notes WHO (2011), half of long-term smokers eventually die of smoking-related causes. Globally tobacco kills the equivalent of one jumbo jet full of passengers crashing every hour of the year. Of the six million people who die each year due to tobacco consumption, about five million are current or former users, but another 600,000 are nonusers who were exposed to secondhand smoke. Tobacco use is the fourth most important risk for disease. If current use trends continue, by 2030 there will be eight million deaths annually caused by tobacco and a total of one billion tobacco-related deaths during the twenty-first century.

Tobacco-related chronic health problems include cardiovascular diseases, respiratory diseases, and cancer, all of which are among the top causes of mortality in the world. These diseases do not kill instantly, rather there is usually a period of years between when people begin using tobacco and the appearance of clear health consequences. The result is not only the loss of individual lives but also the severe impact on households and communities. While the overall prevalence of tobacco use in the world is about four times greater for males than females, among younger users this gender difference is fading, in part because of tobacco manufacturer advertising and other promotions targeting females. Young girls smoke almost as much as their male counterparts. Notably, about one-fourth of young smokers begin tobacco consumption by the age of ten (Global Youth Tobacco Survey Collaborative Group 2002).

The starting point for addressing the global tobacco epidemic is recognizing that it is a completely human-created threat to life. WHO recognizes six strategies as the most effective in preventing tobacco use:

- Develop national mechanisms to monitor tobacco use and prevention efforts.
- Protect nonsmokers from exposure to tobacco (e.g., establish smoke-free zones).
- Provide smoking cessation programs.
- Actively warn smokers and nonsmokers about the dangers of consumption (e.g., put graphic pictures of adverse consequences on cigarette packages).
- Create and enforce bans on tobacco advertising, promotion, and sponsorship.
- Place significant levels of taxation on tobacco.

Developed in response to the globalization of the tobacco epidemic, the World Health Organization Framework Convention on Tobacco Control (FCTC), which was adopted in 2003 at WHO's 56th World Health Assembly, is the world's first global health treaty focused on limiting tobacco promotion and use around the world. The tobacco industry, as a result, has attempted to stop or at least weaken the FCTC. For example, Big Tobacco heavily lobbied the German government to derail the German Federal Health Ministry's support of the treaty.

Recently, with the growing awareness of the health risks of tobacco use, anthropological researchers have put energy into the study of tobacco use. In particular, anthropologists have been interested in the social place of tobacco consumption in cultures around the world, and the ways social integration promotes use and its health consequences. For example, a ritualization of smoking that has been described ethnographically involves use of tobacco as an anticipatory rite of passage among subordinated or marginalized social groups, such as youth, women, and ethnic minorities. Tobacco smoking also serves in some societies as a public marker of belonging in a particular group. The social embeddedness of smoking and its involvement in cultural identity formation add to addiction as powerful factors that hinder smoking cessation. Increasingly, anthropologists have looked at tobacco use in light of its emergence as a global commodity in a worldwide marketing campaign.

As anthropologist Ken Stebbins observes, traditional cultural limitations on the quantity and frequency of smoking around the world have been overwhelmed "by aggressive marketing by transnational tobacco companies" (2001:148). In his research, Stebbins has shown how the tobacco industry turned to markets in the developing world to make up for a loss in sales in developed countries. The governments of developing nations often do not have the capacity to contend with Big Tobacco, which is well-schooled in how to get around government restrictions on tobacco imports and promotion. As a result of extensive tobacco advertising in developing nations worldwide tobacco consumption is increasing at a rate of about one percent per year (Stebbins 2001). In Stebbins' words, the tobacco companies "have been making a killing (in more ways than one)" 2001:164) From a global public health perspective, Mark Nichter comments that the upsurge in anthropological research on tobacco consumption is enabling a closer examination of "the role that cultural institutions, values, and processes play in: (1) protecting against smoking, (2) fostering smoking as a normative behavior within particular gender and age cohorts, and (3) affecting the distribution of particular smoking trajectories" across societies (2003:13).

Impacts of Global Alcohol

The broad outlines of the global alcohol epidemic parallel those of tobacco. Health problems that stem from excessive drinking include liver cirrhosis, pancreatitis, various cancers, high blood pressure, and psychological disorders. On top of local alcohol production, Big Alcohol and its well-heeled transnational corporations have moved in recent decades to consolidate the global alcohol market, especially for spirits and beer, but increasingly for wine as well, into the hands of a relatively small number of companies. As Sally Casswell indicates developing nations with large populations and

> high proportions of young people, expanding economies and relatively low rates of alcohol consumption have become a major focus for the global alcohol corporations seeking growth. In these countries, estimates made in 2000 as part of research on the Global Burden of Disease and Injury suggested that alcohol was already the leading cause of disability-adjusted years of life lost. (2011:1205)

The substantial profits reaped by Big Alcohol have funded extensive drinking promotion in key markets worldwide, making alcohol products among the most heavily marketed commodities internationally. New products are continually being developed to target specific market niches (e.g., youth, ethnic minorities) (Singer 2008a). As a result, "There is an urgent need to recognize that national governments face an increasingly difficult task in developing and defending policy that will actually affect the levels of alcohol-related harm" (Casswell 2011:1207).

This is doubly so because many drinkers also smoke, and smoking and drinking often occur together. A growing body of research shows that the metabolites of smoking and drinking interact syndemically in the body to drive cardiovascular disease, stroke, cancer, and other disease progression as well as mortality (Hart et al. 2010). A diet high in carbohydrates and sugar, an increasingly common pattern globally, contributes to this adverse synergy. This body of research underlines the importance of studying the global market of consumable commodities and its impacts on health-related behavior and health status. More broadly, this research confirms the importance of a global health perspective, as changing patterns of smoking, drinking, and eating throughout the world are tied to corporate globalization, the flow of consumable commodities, and the idealization of using Western goods, including seeing their use as a pathway to modernity.

CONCLUSION

All of the threats to health discussed in this chapter present significant and mounting challenges to global health and the capacity of health activists and institutions to be effective in improving the health of the world's populations. These challenges underline the vital importance of international collaboration, coordination, and preparedness in an increasingly intertwined global world in which health and health resources are inequitably distributed, along with the health consequences of emergencies, armed conflict, biohazards, displacement, and mind-altering drugs.

Chapter Six

A Brighter or Bleaker Future for Global Health?

In the broadest terms, the goals of global health are simple and direct: to address the pressing health challenges around the world while laying the foundation for a healthier future. How to achieve these goals is the hard part. As Ruth Levine indicates, "The magnitude and profundity of current health challenges facing the developing world—from AIDS to chronic malnutrition to the looming threat of tobacco-related cancers—can seem daunting" (2007:xiii).

ARE WE ON THE ROAD TO A HEALTHIER WORLD?

Notably, the book edited by Ruth Levine quoted above is entitled *Case Studies in Global Health: Millions Saved.* The book presents a series of successful global health programs implemented around the world. Yet, it is amply clear that advances made in improving global health are fragile at best. As Michel Sidibé, executive director of the Joint United Nations Program on HIV/AIDS, writes:

> The gains that have been made—improvements in maternal health, strides towards combating HIV and AIDS, malaria and other diseases and reductions in child mortality—are balancing tentatively on a precipice, at risk from large and sometimes seemingly impossible challenges. . . . The number of people newly infected with HIV continues to outpace the number of people placed on antiretroviral treatment. Drug resistant levels of tuberculosis have hit the highest level ever. An annual report recently released by

> UNAIDS and the Kaiser Family Foundation revealed that funding disbursements from donor governments for the AIDS response in low- and middle income countries fell in 2010, dropping 10% from the previous year's level. Left unchecked the twin challenges of climate change and non-communicable diseases will have a devastating impact on the future outlook of global health. (2011:24)

While the contemporary fragility of global health is worldwide, at particular risk are the people who live in the poorest nations and the poorest sectors of all nations, rich and poor alike. As seen throughout this book, wealth is without doubt the single greatest broad determinant of health in the world. Thus, to assess major health problems and health needs, countries are commonly classified into income groups: "high income" refers to countries with a gross national income (GNI) per capita of at least $12,476; "middle income" countries have a GNI per capita of $1,026–$4,035; and "low-income" countries have a GNI per capita of under $1,025 (World Bank 2012). The greatest health burden, not surprisingly, falls on the low-income countries, which, as seen in the earlier discussion of food riots, have many people living on the edge. Wealth disparity (across and within nations) and other expressions of social inequality (e.g., gender discrimination, social construction of pariah populations) are not only primary determinants of the quality of the lives people lead but also of whether or not they live at all.

According to WHO (2007), in the lowest income countries of the world fewer than one-fourth of all people reach the age of 70 (compared to more than two-thirds in high-income countries), and almost one-third of all deaths occur among children who are under 14 years of age. Although cardiovascular disease—which has a significant linkage to tobacco use—comprises the leading cause of death in poor nations, claiming about six million lives a year, infectious diseases (especially HIV/AIDS), lung infections, tuberculosis, diarrheal diseases, and malaria collectively take more lives (over eight million annually) than any other cause. Complications of pregnancy and childbirth are also leading causes of death for women and infants in low-income countries. Unnecessary illness and deaths due to violence; conflict; global climate change; displacement; and use of tobacco, alcohol, and illicit drugs are of growing importance.

Contemplating the many millions of people who die unnecessarily each year—in the sense that the means for effectively preventing or addressing the diseases and conditions that kill them already are in hand—can be demoralizing. Also demoralizing is the fact that the natural and social resources of the world—(adequate food and housing, clean water, education, and freedom from physical threat and emotional trauma)—are so inequitably distributed. While some people have the best of everything that is available in terms of material wealth and quality-of-life experience, others live in dangerous slums,

Living on the economic edge, Iquitos, Peru. (Merrill Singer)

eke out a living scavenging garbage dumps, suffer enduring malnutrition, and die of readily treatable infectious diseases. Add to this picture the fact that we face rising health threats from anthropogenic global warming, mounting dangers from multiple other forms of human-caused ecosystem degradation, and wars that intentionally target civilians as often or more than armed combatants. Without question, focusing intensely for any length of time on the many diseases and other growing threats to health and human well-being in the world, and their ultimate causes, can produce a gloomy mood, fatigue, hopelessness, as well as an immobilizing sense of powerlessness in one's ability to make any difference in the world. This disheartening response can be magnified by feelings of personal responsibility because we still drive cars that pollute the air, we are not shrinking our carbon footprint, we may take risks with our own health, and we lead contradictory lives (e.g., enjoying a long warm shower in water that we know is far cleaner and more plentiful than many people have available to drink over the course of days). In a sense, we face a dual health crisis in the world today. We live in a time of global health fragility and nervous uncertainty, and we have grown weary of having to face multiple and multiplying crises. Is there a way out of our dual dilemma of global health fragility and global health fatigue?

David Gessner, a well-known nature writer, suggests an approach to environmentalism that has relevance for global health. He writes that in light of the weighty problems we face in our relationship with the environment (which also have implications for global health) clearly "it is time to do something. But what to do when there are so many catastrophes?" (2011:8). By way of an answer, he cites the words of Boston-area environmental activist Dan Driscoll, who told him,

> We are all hypocrites. None of us are consistent. The problem is that we let that fact stop us. We worry that if we fight for nature [or, as we promote in this book, for improved world health] people will say, "But you still drive a car," or "You fly a lot," or "You're a consumer too." And that stops us in our tracks. It's almost as if admitting that we are hypocrites lets people off the hook. . . . What we need are more hypocrites. . . . We need hypocrites who aren't afraid of admitting it but will still fight for the environment. We don't need some sort of pure movement run by pure people. We need hypocrites. (Gessner 2011:8)

The same can be said for working on behalf of the cause of global health; the issues are many, and people with an interest in making a difference in global health may feel overwhelmed. It is possible, however, to have a positive and measurable impact by focusing on specific aspects and issues in global health and gaining expertise and experience in these areas (Levine 2007). Ultimately, far-reaching and enduring change across global health issues, especially with regard to the grave health challenges of developing countries and regions, requires collective action and a willingness to challenge prevailing structures of social and economic inequality. It is possible within this context, and while working toward this end, for individuals to engage in meaningful work on smaller issues that contribute to diminishing human suffering.

CASE STUDY
An Anthropological Approach to Treating MDR-TB

The anthropological paradigm offers a viable and proven approach for addressing specific issues in global health, as seen in the case of global health response to the emergence and spread of multidrug-resistant tuberculosis (MDR-TB, which is defined as strains of TB that have come to be resistant to at least two of the most commonly used TB drugs). In the global health community, early response to the emergence of MDR-TB was that while individuals infected with drug-resistant strains could be effectively treated in wealthy countries with strong health care infrastructures and large health care budgets, this was not feasible in resource-poor areas of the world. Since MDR-TB was so expensive to treat, attempts to do so in poor countries would eat up available resources needed to treat nonresistant strains of TB, which were rapidly spreading there. It was argued that the combination of expensive laboratory equipment needed for drug susceptibility testing, expensive second-line drugs needed to treat patients with MDR-TB, and the level of patient monitoring and management by costly clinical personnel made MDR-TB treatment financially beyond the reach of poor nations. Some global health experts also asked, how would resource-poor countries properly manage the treatment of MDR-TB cases, which require treatment for 12–24 months, when they already had difficulty managing and daily monitoring medical adherence among TB patients for the six-month period needed for non-drug-resistant TB treatment?

In the midst of the emergence of these attitudes about the treatment of MDR-TB, a nongovernmental organization called Partners-in-Health (PIH), founded and directed by several physician-anthropologists, initiated a small project designed to treat "chronic" TB patients living in an impoverished shantytown in northern Lima, Peru. PIH clinicians soon discovered the presence of MDR-TB among their patients. As a result, in 1996, PIH modified its usual approach to community-based TB treatment, which had been developed in rural Haiti (Kim et al. 2005). This effort began with a trial with approximately 50 TB patients. As contrasted with what had become standard TB treatment—an approach called DOTS (Directly Observed Treatment Short course)—Lima TB patients in the new PIH program received drug treatment that was individually tailored to the strain of TB that afflicted them. All patients were assigned a trained outreach worker who also lived in the shantytown and visited them in their homes daily to verify that they were taking their medications properly. Outreach workers collected basic clinical, epidemiological, and ethnographic data, which provided them with the ability to recognize adverse reactions to medications. Outreach workers also provided emotional and social support to patients, including, if needed, nutritional and monetary assistance (Sweetland et al. 2002). This form of home-based care aided in the screening of patient social contacts and family members at risk for MDR-TB infection.

PIH's anthropologically informed approach emerged as a model for treatment of MDR-TB in a poor setting, but the announcement of the program's success "was met at first with a great deal of skepticism in the international health community" (Kim et al. 2005:849) as was the subsequent PIH call for universal treatment of MDR-TB among the global poor based on the success of their program. Being ethnographers, members of the PIH team

> searched for ways of understanding more fully the positions of our critics and interlocutors. . . . In the past, we had studied the experiences and explanatory frameworks of people sick with TB; now we were seeking to "study up," as [anthropologist] Laura Nader had suggested years ago. . . . The fates of many were in the hands of policy makers who were work-

ing from assumptions quite different from our own. . . . Short-sighted policies [can] inadvertently lead to non-treatment of the destitute sick.

Research by other clinic teams have affirmed PIH's findings on the respectable cure rates for their approach, the feasibility of implementing it in low-income settings, its cost effectiveness, and its ability to achieve good rates of patient adherence. The PIH team concluded: "Treatment of MDR-TB is simply one small example of how the rich, often arbitrarily, construct barriers to health for the poor" (Kim et al. 2005:857).

By using a community-based approach that rested on the use of outreach workers who were culturally and socially matched to patients, the collection of ethnographic data, and a study-up–oriented analysis of the pharmaceutical policy arena, as well as a deep commitment to the well-being of every patient, the PIH strategy affirmed the value of an anthropological perspective in global health.

CAREERS FOR ANTHROPOLOGISTS IN GLOBAL HEALTH

The diverse, widespread, and acute biosocial challenges that comprise global health and the international effort to improve health around the world have created a range of career opportunities for people trained in anthropology. Potential employers include United Nations programs (e.g., the World Health Organization) or regional health development organizations (e.g., Pan American Health Organization); international, regional or local health NGOs (nongovernment organizations) like Partners-in-Health (info@pih.org), Anthrologica (http://www.anthrologica.com/about.html), American Friends Service Committee (http://www.afsc.org/about), and FHI360 (http://www.fhi360.org/en/AboutFHI/index.htm); private consulting firms like Context-based Research Group (http://contextresearch.com/context/howuse/howuse_index.cfm); government health agencies (e.g., departments of health); independent health research institutes (e.g., the Institute for Community Research, International Center for Research on Women); and the many public and private foundations working in health issues.

According to Nils Daulaire, speaking as the president of the Global Health Council, the world's largest membership alliance of global health organizations, "One of the challenges . . . is that there are a lot of people entering this area from the clinical and the research side. . . . And although both of those are important contributors to the mix, they are not the most critical elements to make a difference to the lives of the 2 billion poorest people in next decade" (quoted in Gewin

2007:349). The skills in demand, he emphasizes, are management, cultural understanding, and an anthropological viewpoint. Similarly, states Harold Jaffe, an internationally recognized scientist and public health expert at the Centers for Disease Control, behavioral scientists, economists, and anthropologists can "play a role equally important to medical doctors" in global health (quoted in Gewin 2007:348). Adds Michael Merson, director of the Global Health Institute at Duke University and former head of the UN Global AIDS Program: "Global health is prevention of disease, not simply treatment" (quoted in Gewin 2007). Merson is well aware of the skills that anthropologists bring to the table, as he helped found Yale University's Center for Interdisciplinary Research on AIDS. In this effort, he reached out to anthropologists working on AIDS to involve them in the national and international work of the center in studying and combating this disease.

Exemplary of available career tracks in global health for anthropologists is the work carried out by CDC, which employs a broad group of over 500 social and behavioral scientists, "individuals who possess diverse backgrounds in psychology, sociology, anthropology, health communications, geography, social work and demography" (CDC 2009). According to the chair of CDC's Behavioral and Social Science Working Group, Janet Heitgerd, "Behavioral and social scientists are found in all Centers and many Coordinating Centers. The National Center for HIV, STD, and TB Prevention (NCHSTP) has the largest number of these scientists, while the National Center for Injury Prevention and Control (NCIPC) has the largest percentage" (CDC 2009). The behavioral and social scientists are involved in a wide range of activities that include programs that develop and evaluate health behavior surveillance systems, public health intervention initiatives, and health promotion and health communication efforts using both quantitative and qualitative research and implementation methods. For example, Mary Spink Neumann, an anthropologist at CDC, works on replicating effective public health programs in HIV/AIDS. Neumann's straightforward advice to students interested in going into a behavioral field in public health is to "absorb all that you can in your education and experiences to increase your job flexibility, and learn to write clearly and simply with correct grammar, spelling, and punctuation" (CDC 2009).

Other important performance skills taught in departments of anthropology that are useful in finding employment in global health include careful record keeping; attention to details; analytical reading and thinking; keen observation skills; and qualitative and quantitative research methodology ability. In addition, having international experience is an important asset in seeking global health employment. Reports Daulaire: "There is nothing early in one's career as valuable as prolonged field experience to prove you can handle the hardships of living in often difficult situations" (quoted in Gewin 2007:349).

There are various ways to get international experience, including campus-managed overseas education programs and international non-government volunteer programs (such as volunteering for building projects, volunteering in an orphanage, teaching English as a second language, volunteering in a sustainable development program). Internship experience abroad provides invaluable insights and networking opportunities and serves as an important step in developing a career in global health. Organizations like Global Volunteer Network (www.globalvolunteernetwork.org), International Student Volunteers (www.isvolunteers.org/), Projects Abroad (www.projects-abroad.org), and Volunteering Solutions (www.volunteeringsolutions.com) offer opportunities for international internship and volunteer experience. Many other venues for gaining international experience through a volunteer organization can be found at Go Abroad.com (http://www.goabroad.com/volunteer-abroad).

Specialized training (e.g., in medical anthropology) can be a good starting point for a career in global health. In addition, some universities (e.g., Case Western Reserve University) offer a Certificate in Global Health for anthropology majors. Another option is getting a dual Anthropology and Masters in Public Health degree, which is offered at a number of universities (e.g., University of Chicago, University of Connecticut, University of Pittsburgh, University of South Florida, and University of Iowa).

Other sources of information on anthropological careers in global health include the Career Center at the American Anthropological Association (http://www.aaanet.org/profdev/), the Society for Applied Anthropology (http://www.sfaa.net/sfaajobs.html), the Royal Anthropological Institute (http://www.therai.org.uk/), the Canadian Anthropological Society (http://www.cas-sca.ca/), and the Australian Anthropological Society (http://www.aas.asn.au/).

Finally, we maintain that it is vital to retain a critical perspective and a willingness to challenge conventional wisdoms, structures of inequality, and politically motivated positions that seek to focus attention on changing individual behaviors and largely ignore stark social inequalities. The ultimate objective is not to sustain the status quo or even to be satisfied with the kinds of minor improvements achievable through a liberal reformist agenda.

The goal is world health, and that demands enormous advances in achieving social justice across multiple social domains. Anthropological contributions to attaining this outcome can only partially be undertaken with the tools of research. Additionally, there is a need, as exemplified by the life of Martin Luther King, Jr., "for active immersion in social struggles, collaborating [with social movements for change], building new forms of engagement, and tackling issues of power, violence, and inequality that combine to produce increasingly miserable conditions of existence for most people on this planet" (Forte 2011:8).

Glossary

Anthropological lens—seeing human behavior as a cultural expression within in complex set of immediate and ultimate determinants

Anthropological paradigm—the anthropological approach to understanding human behavior and society involving an emphasis on culture, social and environmental culture, and location within a wider global system

Armed combat—warfare, especially involving significant levels of unintentional but also intentional civilian casualties

Basic survival needs—the survival need for adequate diet, clean air, potable water, sanitation, housing, and health care

Biohazard—infectious agents or hazardous biological materials that present a risk or potential threat to the health of humans, animals or the environment

Biomonitoring—assessing exposure to and body storage of toxins; the measurement of the body burden of toxic substances

Biosocial—the complex interaction of biological and social factors in determining human behavior and experience

Body burden—the total amount of all toxic substances or a specific toxic substance present in a human body at a given point in time

Cluster sampling method—a health research method used to test an intervention and compared to a reference population of healthy individuals

Complex humanitarian emergency (CHE)—a humanitarian crisis in which there is total or extensive breakdown of authority and order, which requires an international response that goes beyond the mandate or capacity of any single existing program

Critical medical anthropology—a theoretical framework within medical anthropology that emphasizes the role of social inequality and the exercise of power in the determination of human health

Cultural logic—using shared culturally constituted assumptions in implementing personal actions and interpreting the actions of others

Culture—shared frameworks for understanding and acting in the world acquired through socialization within a social group

Cultural inconsonance—the stress experienced from wanting and culturally valuing social markers of success

Cultural relativism—avoiding judging the behaviors of one society by the standards and values of another

Dual health burden—refers to population health involving a significant threat from both infectious and chronic diseases

Economic globalization—the development of new production, marketing, and other financial mechanisms (e.g. transnational organizations and capital and commodity flows) that tie all nations together economically

Ecosyndemic—an environmental mediated adverse interaction of two or more diseases that increase the human health burden

Emic—the cultural insider's perspective on the world and society

Enculturated—having learned to be a member in a cultural system

Endemic—a disease that remains in a population over a long period of time

Environmental health—quality of health produced by the interaction of environmental risks and opportunities (e.g., resources)

Environmental justice—the fair treatment and meaningful involvement of all people regardless of ethnicity or social status in the development, implementation, and enforcement of fair environmental policies

Environmental racism—policies and practices that unfairly distribute environmental hazards and industrial hazardous waste in areas that are disproportionately home to marginalized ethnic minorities

Environmental risk factors—specific ways environmental features and events threaten human health

Epidemic—a notable jump in the number of cases of a particular disease within a population

Ethnocentrism—seeing the world only through one's own cultural lens and hence negatively appraising other ways of being and behaving

Ethnography—the core methodology of anthropology involving immersion and participant observation in social environments; often the foundation for various other forms of data collection

Experience-near—a term used in anthropology to refer to the value of the ethnographic approach in getting as near as possible to people's experience of events and interactions in their life

Food deserts—geographic areas—usually low-income—that have no grocery stores within several miles

Food insecurity—situations in which access to nutritionally adequate and safe foods is limited or not dependable

Global alcohol and tobacco epidemics—health epidemics produced by globalization and the neoliberal breakdown of barriers to the free world flow of commodities, including those that carry a significant health burden like alcohol and tobacco

Global climate change—as used in the contemporary period, anthropogenically caused greenhouse gas blanketing of Earth that leads to increasingly rising global temperature over time and numerous, often adverse, environmental changes

Global health—understanding health in the world, and within any location, as interconnected within and across societies

Globalization—worldwide social transformation set in motion by economic forces involving international flows of commodities, communication technologies, people, cultural elements and lifestyles, and diseases

Green revolution—an attempt to address world food needs by introducing industrial and privatized farming technologies to developing nations, including private ownership of seeds and reliance on chemical fertilizers and pesticides

Health culture—the pattern of health beliefs and practices found in a cultural system

Health disparities—differences in health between social groups

Health inequalities—health disparities that are caused by social inequalities

Health transition—the change in time in a population involving control of infectious diseases and emergence of chronic diseases as the primary source of illness

Health-based environmental indicators—quantitative measures of environmental impacts on human health

Human habitat—the social, political, and ecological worlds we inhabit

Hunger—in the short-term, a body-triggered painful sensation of needing to eat

International health—an older term used to talk about varied health conditions in the world

Junk food islands—high concentrations of fast-food chains and convenience stores in low-income neighborhoods

Malnutrition—as a physical state in which an inadequate diet, including lack of protein and/or calories and micronutrients, leads to damage in natural bodily systems and abilities like growth, pregnancy, lactation, learning, work, and resisting and recovering from infection

Medical anthropology—a branch of anthropology focused on studying health, health-related behaviors, and healing practices across the world

Mortality survey—the calculation of crude death rates suffered by a population during an emergency

Neoliberalism—an economic philosophy that maintains that the market, and not governments, should determine the price of goods, including food staples, medicines, education, health care, and housing

Obesogenic environments—built environments that promote obesity among people who live in them

Pandemic—the spread of a disease across human populations within a region, multiple regions or worldwide

Pluralea—two or more adversely interacting environmental crises that enhance the human health burden

Population health—health patterns at the level of whole populations

Refugee and otherwise displaced populations—people who are pushed from their previous or traditional place of residence by war, conflict, environmental change, or other factors into new places within or beyond their national borders

Resilience—the ability to cope with and adjust to new health, environmental, and social challenges

Social determinants of health—social structures and conditions that cause particular health problems

Solastalgia—a label of psychological distress among people living in a disrupted and rapidly changing environment with new threats and challenges

Stratified hygiene—unequal access to sanitation facilities based on social and economic inequality

Structural adjustment policies (SAPs)—policies often mandated by international lending institutions that require developing countries to adhere to neoliberal tenants and significantly cut government involvement in a nation's economy

Structural violence—a combination of various forms of discrimination, maltreatment, and oppression foisted upon the poor and marginalized through the major institutions of society

Stunted—chronic malnourishment that produces deficits in height-for-age measurements

Syndemic—the adverse interaction between two or more diseases resulting in an increased health burden for the affected population, usually as a consequence of social inequalities that produce disease clusters in marginalized, stigmatized, and/or impoverished populations

Underweight—acute and chronic malnourishment that produces deficits in weight-for-age measurements

Unnatural disasters—catastrophes ultimately caused by human impacts on the environment

Wasted—suffering from acute malnutrition sufficient to produce weight-for-height deficits

References

Aguilera, Francisco, Josefina Méndez, Eduardo Pásaro, and Blanca Laffon. 2010. Review on the Effects of Exposure to Spilled Oils on Human Health. *Journal of Applied Toxicology* 30: 291–301.

American Public Health Association. 2011. *Climate Change: Mastering the Public Health Role*. New York: APHA.

Albrecht, Glenn, Gina-Maree Sartore, Linda Connor, Nick Higginbotham, Sonia Freeman, Brian Kelly, Helen Stain, Anne Tonna, and Georgia Pollard. 2007. Solastalgia: The Distress Caused by Environmental Change. *Australasian Psychiatry* 15 (Supplement 1): S95–S98.

Alley, Kelly. 2002. *On the Banks of the Ganga: When Wastewater Meets a Sacred River*. Ann Arbor: University of Michigan Press, American Public Health Association.

———. 2011. *Climate Change: Mastering the Public Health Role*. Washington, DC: APHA.

Amon, Joseph. 2010. Lead Poisoning in Nigeria "Unprecedented." Human Rights Watch. Available online at: http://www.hrw.org/en/news/2010/12/02/lead-poisoning-nigeria-unprecedented. Accessed 5/31/11.

Ananias, Patrus. 2009. Implementing the Human Right to Food in Brazil. Available online at: http://www.worldhunger.org/articles/08/hrf/ananias.htm. Accessed 3/2/12.

Anastario, Michael, Nadine Shehab, and Lynn Lawry. 2009. Increased Gender-based Violence Among Women Internally Displaced in Mississippi 2 Years Post-Hurricane Katrina. *Disaster Medicine and Public Health Preparedness* 3: 18–26.

Anderson, Warwick. 2006. *Colonial Pathologies: American Tropical Medicine, Race, and Hygiene in the Philippines*. Durham, NC: Duke University Press.

Baer, Hans. 2010. The Impact of the War Machine on Global Warming and Health: A Political-Ecological Perspective. In *The War Machine and Global Health*, Merrill Singer and G. Derrick Hodge (eds.), pp. 157–177. Lanham, MD: AltaMira.

Baer, Hans, and Thomas Reuter. 2011. The Global Movement for a Safe climate and Environmental Sustainability. *The Australian Journal of Anthropology* 22(2): 1–5.

Baer, Hans, and Merrill Singer. 2009. *Global Warming and the Political Economy of Health: Emerging Crises and Systematic Solutions*. Walnut Creek, CA: Left Coast Press.

Bangladesh Department of the Environment. 2002. *Bangladesh: State of the Environment Report in 2002*. Dhaka, Bangladesh: Department of the Environment.

Barlow, Maude, and Tony Clarke. 2004. Water Privatization. Global Policy Forum. Available online at: http://www.globalpolicy.org/component/content/article/209/43398.html. Accessed 6/9/11.

Bell, Michelle L., and Devra L. Davis. 2001. Reassessment of the Lethal London Fog of 1952: Acute and Chronic Consequences of Acute exposure to Air Pollution. *Environmental Health Perspectives* 109 (Supplement 3): 389–394.

Bellisari, Anna. 2013. *The Obesity Epidemic in North America: Connecting Biology and Culture*. Long Grove, IL: Waveland Press.

Bender, Morris A., Thomas R. Knutson, Robert E. Tuleya, Joseph J. Sirutis, Gabriel A. Vecchi, Stephen T. Garner, and Isaac M. Held. 2010. Modeled Impact of Anthropogenic Warming on the Frequency of Intense Atlantic Hurricanes. *Science* 327(5964): 454–458.

Berkes, Fikret, and Jolly, Dyanna. 2001. Adapting to Climate Change: Social-Ecological Resilience in a Canadian Western Arctic Community. *Conservation Ecology* 5(2): 18. Available online at: http://www.consecol.org/vol5/iss2/art18. Accessed 5/22/11.

Biermann, Frank, and Ingrid Boas. 2007. Preparing for a Warmer World: Toward a Global Governance System to Protect Climate Refugees. Global Governance Working Paper No. 33. Available online at http://www.glogov.org/?pageid=22. Accessed 7/14/11.

Birn, Anne-Emanuelle, Yogan Pillay, and Timothy H. Holtz. 2009. *Textbook of International Health: Global Health in a Dynamic World*. 3rd ed. Oxford, UK: Oxford University Press.

Black, R., S. Morris, and J. Bryce. 2003. Where and Why Are 10 Million Children Dying Every Year? *Lancet* 361: 2226–2234.

Blacksmith Institute. 2007. *The World's Ten Most Polluted Places*. New York: Blacksmith Institute.

Boas, Franz. 1928. *Anthropology and Modern Life*. New York: Norton.

Bodley, John. 2008. *Victims of Progress*. Lanham, MD: AltaMira.

Bond, David. 2011. The Science of Catastrophe: Making Sense of the BP Oil Spill. *Anthropology Now* 3(1): 36–46.

Bowermaster, Jon. 2007. Global Warming Changing Inuit Lands, Lives, Arctic Expedition. *National Geographic News*. Available online at: http://news.nationalgeographic.com/news/2007/05/070515-inuit-arctic.html. Accessed 5/20/11.

Bradshaw, Debbie, and Nadine Nannan. 2003. Health Status. Available online at: http://www.hst.org.za/uploads/files/chap4_03.pdf. Accessed 9/11/12.

Brennan, Richard, and Robin Nandy. 2001. Complex Humanitarian Emergencies: A Major Global Health Challenge. *Emergency Medicine* 13: 147–156.

Brown, Theodore, Marcos Cueto, and Elizabeth Fee. 2006. The World Health Organization and the Transition From "International" to "Global" Public Health. *American Journal of Public Health* 96(1): 62–72.

Browne, Andrew. 2004. Tsunami's Aftermath: On Asia's Coasts, Progress Destroys Natural Defenses. *Wall Street Journal*, December 31, p. A5.

Budrys, Grace. 2010. *Unequal Health: How Inequality Contributes to Health and Illness*. Lanham, MD: Rowman & Littlefield.

Burkle, F. 1999. Lessons Learnt and Future Expectations of Complex Emergencies. *British Medical Journal* 319: 422–426.

Castro, Arachu. 2010. Social Inequalities and Dengue Transmission in Latin America. In *Plagues and Epidemics: Infected Spaces Past and Present*, D. Ann Herring and Alan Swedlund (eds.), pp. 231–249. Oxford, UK: Berg.

Casswell, Sally. 2011. Alcohol Harm—The Urgent Need for a Global Response. *Addiction* 106(7): 1205–1207.

CDC (Centers for Disease Control and Prevention). 2002. Injuries and Illnesses among New York City Fire Department Rescue Workers after Responding to the World Trade Center Attacks. *Morbidity and Mortality Weekly Repor*t 51 (special issue): 1–5.

———. 2009. CDC Social and Behavioral Scientists. *Careers at CDC*. Available online at: http://www.cdc.gov/about/opportunities/careers/socialBehavioral.htm. Accessed 3/3/12.

Centre for Research on the Epidemiology of Disasters. 2011. *Annual Disaster Statistic Review 2011*. Brussels: Institute for Health and Society of the University of Louvain.

Cernea, M., and C. McDowell. 2000. *Risks and Reconstruction: Experiences of Resettlers and Refugees*. Washington, DC: The World Bank.

Chaiken, Miriam, Richard J. Dixon, Colette Powers, and Erica Wetzler. 2009. Asking the Right Questions: Community-based Strategies to Combat Hunger. *NAPA Bulletin* 32(1): 42–54.

Checker, Melissa. 2005. *Polluted Promises: Environmental Racism and the Search for Justice in a Southern Town*. New York: New York University Press.

———. 2008. Withered Memories: Naming and Fighting Environmental Racism in Georgia. In *New Landscapes of Inequality: Neoliberalism and the Erosion of Democracy in America*, Jane Collins, Micaela di Leonardo, and Brett Williams (eds.). Santa Fe, NM: School for Advanced Research Press.

Cherrington, Mark. 2008. Indigenous Peoples Take Action against Climate Change. *Anthropology News* 49(6): 31.

Chilkov, Nalini. 2010. Everyday Exposures to Toxic Chemicals: Is Your Family Safe? *Huffpost Health*. Available online at: http://www.huffingtonpost.com/nalini-chilkov/everyday-exposures-to-toxic-chemicals_b_796520.html. Accessed 5/27/11.

Chronic Disease News. 2009. Chronic Disease: an emerging priority in Bangladesh. *Chronic Disease News* 1(1): 1–6.

Cohen, Mark, and George Armelagos, Eds. 1984. *Paleopathology at the Origins of Agriculture*. Waltham, MA: Elsevier Science & Technology Books.

Coker, Christopher. 2004. War and Disease. 21st Century Trust. Available online at: http://www.21stcenturytrust.org/coker2.html. Accessed 1/15/11.

Commission for Racial Justice. 1987. *Toxic Wastes and racism in the United States: A National Report on the Racial and Socio-Economic characteris-*

tics of Communities with Hazardous Waste Sites. New York: United Church of Christ.

Constitution of the World Health Organization. 2006. *Basic Documents.* 45th ed. Supplement, October. Available online at: www.who.int/governance/eb/who_constitution_en.pdf. Accessed 1/15/12.

Coreil, Jeannine, Linda Whiteford, and Diego Salazar. 1997. The Household Ecology of Disease Transmission: Dengue Fever in the Dominican Republic. In *The Anthropology of Infectious Disease: International Health Perspectives,* Marcia Inhorn and Peter Brown (eds.), pp. 143–171. Amsterdam, The Netherlands: Gordon and Breach.

Corvalan, Carlos, Simon Hales, and Anthony McMichael. 2005. *Ecosystems and Human Well-Being: Health Synthesis, a Report of the Millennium Ecosystem Assessment.* Geneva, Switzerland: WHO.

Craddock, Susan. 2004. Introduction: Beyond Epidemiology. In *HIV and AIDS in Africa: Beyond Epidemiology,* Ezekiel Kalipeni, Susan Craddock, Joseph Oppong, and Jayati Ghosh (eds.), pp. 1–10. Malden, MA: Blackwell.

Crate, Susan. 2009. Gone the Bull of Winter? Contemplating Climate Change's Cultural Implications in Northeastern Siberia, Russia. In *Anthropology and Climate Change: From Encounters to Action,* Susan Crate and Mark Nuttall (eds.), pp. 139–152. Walnut Creek, CA: Left Coast Press.

Crutzen, Paul. 2002. Geology of Mankind. *Nature* 415: 23.

Daley, Suzanne. 2011. Fiscal Crisis Takes Toll on Health of Greeks. *New York Times,* December 27, p. A4.

Daniell, James. 2011. Damaging Earthquakes Database 2010. CATDAT. Available online at: http://earthquake-report.com/wp-content/uploads/2011/03/CATDAT-EQ-Data-1st-Annual-Review-2010-James-Daniell-03-03-2011.pdf. Accessed 5/28/11.

Davies, Catriona. 2010. Inuit Lives and Diets Change as Ice Shifts. CNN, December 30. Available online at: http://articles.cnn.com/2010-12-30/world/inuit.impact.climate.change_1_ice-inuit-junk-food?_s=PM:WORLD. Accessed 9/12/12

de Wet, Chris. 2006. Risk, Complexity, and Local Initiative in Forced Resettlement Outcomes. In *Toward Improving Outcomes in Development-Induced Involuntary Resettlement Projects.* C. de Wet (ed.), pp. 180–202. Oxford, UK: Berghahn.

Donovan, Cynthia, and Jaquelino Massingue. 2007. Illness, Death, and Macronutrients: Adequacy of rural Mozambican Household Production of Macronutrients in the Face of HIV/AIDS. *Food and Nutrition Bulletin* 28 (Supplement 2): S331–S338.

Dressler, William. 1999. Modernization, Stress and Blood Pressure. New Directions in Research. *Human Biology* 71: 583–605.

———. 2011. Culture and the Stress Process. In *A Companion to Medical Anthropology.* Merrill Singer and Pamela I. Erickson (eds.), pp. 119–157. Malden, MA: Blackwell.

Du, W., G. J. FitzGerald, M. Clark, and X. Y. Hou. 2010. Health Impacts of Floods. *Prehospital and Disaster Medicine* 25(3): 265–72.

Duhigg, Charles. 2009. Millions in U.S. Drink Dirty Water, Records Show. *New York Times,* December 7. Available online at: http://www.nytimes.com/2009/12/08/business/energy-environment/08water.html?pagewanted=all. Accessed 7/2/12.

Dussart, Francoise. 2010. "It is hard to be sick now": Diabetes and the Reconstruction of Indigenous Sociality. *Anthropologica* 52(1): 67–76.

Edgerton, Robert. 1992. *Sick Societies: Challenging the Myth of Primitive Harmony*. New York: The Free Press.

Elliott, James, and Jeremy Pais. 2006. Race, Class, and Hurricane Katrina: Social Differences in Human Responses to Disaster. *Social Science Research* 35: 295–321.

Ennis-McMillan, Michael. 2006. *A Precious Liquid: Drinking Water and Culture in the Valley of Mexico*. Belmont, CA: Thomson Higher Education.

Eriksen, Thomas. 2001. *Small Places, Large Issues: An Introduction to Social and Cultural Anthropology*. 2nd ed. London: Pluto Press.

Erickson, Pamela. 2008. *Ethnomedicine*. Long Grove, IL: Waveland Press.

Evans-Pritchard, E. E. 1940. *The Nuer: A Description of the Modes of Livelihood and Political Institutions of a Nilotic People*. Oxford, UK: Clarendon Press.

Ezzati, Majid, Alan Lopez, Anthony Rodgers, Christopher Murray. 2004. *Comparative Quantification of Health Risks: Global and Regional Burden of Disease Attributable to Selected Major Risk Factors*. Geneva, Switzerland: World Health Organization.

Fadiman, Anne. 1997. *The Spirit Catches You and You Fall Down*. New York: Farrar, Strauss, and Giroux.

Faridkot/Muktsar, Sandeep. Green Revolution's Cancer Train. 2012. *Hardnews*. Available online at: http://www.hardnewsmedia.com/2006/11/648. Accessed 3/1/12.

Farmer, Paul. 2009. On Suffering and Structural Violence: A View from Below. *Race / Ethnicity: Multidisciplinary Global Perspectives* 3(1): 11–28.

———. 2003. *Pathologies of Power: Health, Human Rights and the New War on the Poor*. Berkeley: University of California Press.

Feenstra, Sabiena, Quamrun Nahar, David Pahan, Linda Oskam, and Jan Richardus. 2011. Recent Food Shortage Is Associated with Leprosy Disease in Bangladesh: A Case-Control Study. *PLoS Neglected Tropical Diseases* 5(5): e1029.

Feld, Steven, and Keith Basso, Eds. 1996. *Senses of Place*. Santa Fe: School of American Research Press.

Feldman, S. 2008. Why Overfishing = Global Warming. *Solve Climate News*. Available online at: http://solveclimate.com/blog/20080115/why-overfishing-global-warming. Accessed 4/28/10.

Ferreira Mariana, and Gretchen Lang, Eds. 2006. Indigenous Peoples and Diabetes. In *Community Empowerment and Wellness*, Mariana Ferreira and Gretchen Lang (eds.). Durham, NC: Carolina Academic Press.

Fishman, Steven, Laura Caulfield, Mercedes De Onis, Monika Blössner, Adnan Hyder, Luke Mullany, and Robert Black. 2004. Childhood and Maternal Underweight. In *Comparative Quantification of Health Risks: Global and Regional Burden of Disease Attributable to Selected Major Risk Factors*, Majid Ezzati, Alan Lopez, Anthony Rodgers, and Christopher Murray (eds.), pp. 39–162. Geneva, Switzerland: WHO.

Food and Agriculture Organization. 2002. The Developing World's New Burden: Obesity. Available online at: http://www.fao.org/FOCUS/E/obesity/obes1.htm. Accessed 3/15/12.

Forte, Maxmilian. 2011. Beyond Public Anthropology: Approach Zero. Keynote address delivered by video to the 8th Public Anthropology Conference,

(Re)Defining Paradigms of Praxis, American University, Washington, DC, October 14–16.

Galhardo, R., P. Hastings, and S. Rosenberg, S. 2007. Mutation as a Stress Response and the Regulation of Evolvability. *Critical Reviews in Biochemical and Molecular Biology* 42(5): 399–435.

Garfield, Richard. 2008. The Epidemiology of War. In *War and Public Health*, Barry Levy and Victor Sidel (eds.), pp. 23–36.Washington, DC: American Public Health Association.

Garrett, Laurie. 2001. *The Betrayal of Trust: The Collapse of Global Public Health*. New York: Hyperion.

Geiger, H. Jack. 2002. Racial and Ethnic Disparities in Diagnosis and Treatment: A Review of the Evidence and a Consideration of Causes. In *Unequal Treatment*, Brian Smedley, Adrienne Stith, and Alan Nelson (eds.), pp. 417–454. Washington, DC: National Academies Press.

Geneva Declaration Secretariat. 2008. *Global Burden of Armed Violence*. Geneva, Switzerland: Geneva Declaration Secretariat on Armed Violence and Development.

Gessner, David. 2011. *My Green Manifesto: Down the Charles River in Pursuit of a New Environmentalism*. Minneapolis: Milkweed Editions.

Gewin, Virginia. 2007. The Global Challenge. *Nature* 447: 348–349.

Gezon, Lisa. 2012. *Drug Effects. Khat in Biocultural and Socioeconomic Perspective*. Walnut Creek, CA: Left Coast Press.

Giroux, Henry. 2009, January 14. From Mississippi to Gaza: Killing children with impunity. *Counterpunch*. Available online at: http://www.counterpunch.org/giroux01142009.html. Accessed 1/14/2009.

Gleick, Peter H. 1996. Basic Water Requirements for Human Activities: Meeting Basic Needs. *Water International* 21: 83–92.

Global Humanitarian Forum. 2009. Human Impact Report: Climate Change—The Anatomy of a Silent Crisis. Available online at: http://www.ghf-ge.org. Accessed 5/19/11.

Global Youth Tobacco Survey Collaborative Group. 2002. Tobacco Use among Youth: A Cross Country Comparison. *Tobacco Control* 11: 252–270

Gostin, Lawrence. 2008. Meeting Basic Survival Needs of the World's Least Healthy People: Toward a Framework Convention on Global Health. *The Georgetown Law Journal* 96(2): 331–392.

Gravlee, Clarence, William Dressler, and Russell Bernard. 2005. Skin Color, Social Classification, and Blood Pressure in Southeastern Puerto Rico. *American Journal of Public Health* 95: 2191–2197.

Guarnaccia, Peter, Robert Lewis-Fernandez, Igda Martinez Pincay, Patrick Shrout, Jing Guo, Maria Torres, Glorisa Canino, and Margarita Alegria. 2010. Ataque De Nervios as a Marker of Social and Psychiatric Vulnerability: Results From the NLAAS. *International Journal of Social Psychiatry* 56(3): 298–309.

Hallward, Peter. 2010. Our Role in Haiti's Plight. *The Guardian*, January 13. Available online at: http://www.guardian.co.uk/commentisfree/2010/jan/13/our-role-in-haitis-plight. Accessed 5/28/11.

Hansen, J., M. Sato, R. Ruedy, A. Lacis, and V. Oinas. 2000. Global Warming in the Twenty-First Century: An Alternative Scenario. *Proceeding of the National. Academy of Science* 97: 9875–9880.

Hassan, M. R., A. R. Kabir, A. M. Mahmud, F. Rahman, M. A. Hossain, K. S. Bennoor, M. K. Amin, and M. M. Rahman. 2002. Self-Reported Asthma Symptoms in Children and Adults of Bangladesh: Findings of the National Asthma Prevalence Study. *International Journal of Epidemiology* 31(2): 483–488.

Healthy Lives: Global Health News and Commentary. 2011. *The Leading Causes of Death in Low, Middle and High-Income Countries*. Geneva, Switzerland: WHO.

Herring, D. Ann, and Alan Swedlund. 2010. Plagues and Epidemics in Anthropological Perspective. *In Plagues and Epidemics: Infected Spaces Past and Present*, D. Ann Herring and Alan Swedlund (eds.), pp. 1–19. Oxford, UK: Berg.

Hindu, The. 2010. Most Lead Batteries Do Not End up with Registered Recyclers. October 28, p. 1.

Hart, Carole, George Smith, Laurence Gurer, and Graham Watt. 2010. The Combined Effect of Smoking Tobacco and Drinking Alcohol on Cause-specific Mortality: A 30-Year Cohort Study. *BMC Public Health* 10: 789. doi: 10.1186/1471-2458-10-789.

Holloway, Kris. 2007. *Monique and the Mango Rains. Two Years with a Midwife in Mali*. Long Grove, IL: Waveland Press.

Human Security Research Group. 2009. *Human Security Research Report: The Shrinking Costs of War*. Vancouver, Canada: School for International Studies, Simon Fraser University.

Inter Press Service. 2008. Zimbabwe: Water Crisis and Cholera Funerals, December 4. Available online at: http://www.afrika.no/Detailed/17694.html. Accessed 6/10/11.

Inter-Agency Standing Committee. 2008. Climate Change, Migration and Displacement: Who Will Be Affected? Informal Group on Migration/Displacement and Climate Change of the IASC. Available online at: www.humanitarianinfo.org/iasc. Accessed 2/3/11.

International Consortium of Investigative Journalists. 2003. Cholera and the Age of the Water Barons. Available online at: http://www.oocities.org/waterose_test/water01.html. Accessed 6/10/11.

International Food Policy Research Institute. 2011. The Challenge of Hunger: Taming Price Spikes and Excessive Food Price Volatility. *2011 Global Hunger Index*. Washington, DC: IFPRI. Available online at: http://www.ifpri.org/publication/2011-global-hunger-index. Accessed 9/12/12.

Jacobson, Mark. 2008. On the Causal Link between Carbon Dioxide and Air Pollution Mortality. *Geophysical Research Letters* 35. Available online at: http://europa.agu.org/?view=article&uri=/journals/gl/gl0803/2007GL031101/2007GL031101.xml&t=gl. Accessed 1/15/09.

Jerrett, M., R. Burnett, J. Brook, et al. 2004. Do Socioeconomic Characteristics Modify the Short-Term Association between Air Pollution and Mortality? Evidence from a Zonal Time Series in Hamilton, Canada. *Journal of Epidemiology and Community Health* 58: 31–40.

Johnston, Barbara Rose. 2005. The Commodification of Water and the Human Dimensions of Manufactured Scarcity. In *Globalization, Water and Health: Resource Management in Times of Scarcity*, Linda Whiteford and Scott Whiteford (eds.), pp.133–152. Santa Fe, NM: School of American Research Press.

Kakissis, Joanna. 2010. Environmental Refugees Unable to Return Home. *New York Times*, July 14.

Kamat, Vinay. 2009. The Anthropology of Childhood Malaria in Tanzania. In *Anthropology and Public Health: Bridging Differences in Culture and Society*, Robert Hahn and Marcia Inhorn (eds.), pp. 35–64. Oxford, UK: Oxford University Press.

Khanna, Sunil. 2012. Anthropological Approaches for Understanding the Complexities of the Global Food Crisis. *NAPA Bulletin* 32(1): 193–200.

Klaten Online. 2008. Klaten Farmers Say No to AQUA-Danone Bottled Water Company. Available online at: http://klatenonline.com/klaten/klaten-farmers-say-no-to-aqua-danone-bottled-water-company.htm. Accessed 6/9/11.

Knox, E. G. 2008. Atmospheric Pollutants and Mortalities in English Local Authority Areas. *Journal of Epidemiology and Community Health* 62: 442–447.

Krieger, Nancy. 2001. Theories for Social Epidemiology in the 21st Century: An Ecosocial Perspective. *International Journal of Epidemiology*. 30(4): 668–677.

———. 2003. Does Racism Harm Health? Did Child Abuse Exist Before 1962? On Explicit Questions, Critical Science, and Current Controversies: An Ecosocial Perspective. *American Journal of Public Health* 93(2): 194–199.

———. 2005. *Health Disparities and the Body*. Boston: Harvard School of Public Health.

———. 2007. Why Epidemiologists Cannot Afford to Ignore Poverty. *Epidemiology* 18(6): 658–663.

Labonté, Ronald, and Ted Schrecker. 2007. Globalization and Social Determinants of Health: Introduction and Methodological Background. *Globalization and Health* 3:5. doi: 10.1186/1744-8603-3-5.

Lancet Series on Global Mental Health. 2007. *The Lancet* 370(9590).

Landrigan, Philip, Paul Lioy, George Thurston, Bertrud Berkowitz, L. Chen, Steven Chillrud, Stephen Gavett, Panos Georgopoulos, Alison Geyh, Stephen Levin, Frederica Perera, Stephen Rappaport, and Christopher Small. 2004. Health and Environmental Consequences of the World Trade Center Disaster. *Environmental Health Perspectives* 112(6): doi: 10.1289/ehp.6702

Levine, Ruth. 2007. *Case Studies in Global Health: Millions Saved*. Boston: Jones and Bartlett Publishers.

Levy, Barry, and Victor Sidel, Eds. 2008. *War and Public Health*. 2nd ed. New York: Oxford University Press.

Locke, C. J., K. Southwick, L. McCloskey, and M. Fernández-Esquer. 1996. The Psychological and Medical Sequelae of War in Central American Refugee Mothers and Children. *Archives of Pediatric and Adolescent Medicine* 150(8): 822–828.

Lockman, S., N. Hone, T. Kenyon, M. Mwasekaga, M. Villauthapillai, T. Creek, E. Zell, A. Kirby, W. Thacker, D. Talkington, I. Moura, N. Binkin, L. Clay, and J. Tappero. 2003. Etiology of Pulmonary Infections in Predominantly HIV-Infected Adults with Suspected Tuberculosis, Botswana. *International Journal of Tuberculosis and Lung Disease* 7(8): 714–723.

Machel, Grac'a. 1996. Promotion and Protection of the Rights of Children: Impact of Armed Conflict on Children. United Nations, UNICEF. Available online at: http://www.unicef.org/graca/a51-306_en.pdf. Accessed 1/19/11.

Markowitz, G., and D. Rosner. 2002. *Deceit and Denial: The Deadly Politics of Industrial Pollution*. Berkeley: University of California Press.

Martins, M., F. Fatgati, T. Vespoli, et al. 2004. Influence of Socioeconomic Conditions on Air Pollution Adverse Health Effects in Elderly People: An Analysis of Six Regions in Sao Paulo, Brazil. *Journal of Epidemiology and Community Health* 58: 41–46.

Maternowska, M. Catherine. 2006. *Reproducing Inequities: Poverty and the Politics of Population in Haiti*. New Brunswick, NJ: Rutgers University Press.

Mauderly, J., and J. Samet. 2009. Is There Evidence for Synergy Among Air Pollutants in Causing Health Effects? *Environmental Health Perspectives* 117(1): 1–6.

Maxwell, S., and A. Fernando. 1989. Cash Crops in Developing Countries: The Issues, the Facts, the Policies/Ideas. *World Development* 17(11): 1677–1708.

McCann, David, Ainsley Moore, and Mary-Elizabeth Walker. 2011. The Public Health Implications of Water in Disasters. *World Medical & Health Policy* 3(2): Article 3.

McCartor, Andrew, Dan Becker, David Hanrahan, Bret Ericson Andrea Thomen, Richard, Fuller, Donald Jones, Ira May, and Jack Caravanos. 2010. *World's Worst Pollution Problems Report 2010*. New York: Blacksmith Institute.

McMullin, Juliet. 2009. *The Healthy Ancestor. Embodied Inequality and the Revitalization of Native Hawai'ian Health*. Walnut Creek, CA: Left Coast Press.

McNeil, Bryan. 2011. *Combating Mountaintop Removal: New Directions in the Fight against Big Coal*. Champaign: University of Illinois Press.

Mendenhall, Emily. 2011. The VIDDA Syndemic: Distress and Diabetes in Social and Cultural Context. PhD Dissertation, Department of Anthropology, Northwestern University.

Messer, Ellen. 1998. Conflict as a Cause of Hunger. In *Who's Hungry? And How Do We Know? Food Shortage, Poverty and Deprivation*. L. DeRose, Ellen Messer, and Sara Millman (eds.), pp. 164–180. Tokyo: UN University Press.

———. 2012. Rising Food Prices, Social Mobilizations, and Violence: Conceptual Issues in Understanding and Responding to the Connections Linking Hunger and Violence. *NAPA Bulletin* 32: 12–22.

Messer, Ellen, and Marc Cohen. 2009. US Approaches to Food and Nutrition Rights, 1976–2008. Available online at: http://www.worldhunger.org/articles/08/hrf/messer.htm. Accessed 3/2/12.

Millstein, D., and R. Harley. 2009. Impact of Climate change on Photochemical Air Pollution in Southern California. *Atmospheric Chemistry and Physics* 9(11): 3745–3754.

Mintz, Sidney, and Christine Du Bois. 2002. The Anthropology of Food and Eating. *Annual Review of Anthropology* 31: 99–119.

Mohanty, B. 2005. We Are Like the Living Dead: Farmer Suicides in Maharashtra, Western India. *The Journal of Peasant Studies* 32(2): 243–276.

Moland, Karen Marie, and Astrid Blystad. 2009. Counting on Mother's Love: The Global Politics of Prevention of Mother-to-Child Transmission of HIV in East Africa. In *Anthropology and Public Health: Bridging Differences in Culture and Society*, Robert Hahn and Marcia Inhorn, pp. 447–479. Oxford, UK: Oxford University Press.

Moyers, Bill. 2002. Tobacco Traffic. *NOW*, April 19. Transcript available online at: http://www.pbs.org/now/transcript/transcript114_full.html. Accessed 12/12/10.

Mull, Dorothy. 2000. The Sitala Syndrome: The Cultural Context of Measles Mortality in Pakistan. In *The Anthropology of Infectious Disease: International Health Perspectives*, Marcia Inhorn and Peter Brown (eds.), pp. 299–329. Amsterdam, The Netherlands: Gordon and Breach Publishers.

Nellemann, C., S. Hain, and J. Alder, Eds. 2008. *In Dead Water—Merging of Climate Change with Pollution, Over-Harvest, and Infestations in the World's Fishing Grounds*. Arendal, Norway: United Nations Environment Programme.

Nellemann, C., M. MacDevette, T. Manders, B. Eickhout, B. Svihus, A. Prins, and B. P. Kaltenborn, Eds. 2009. *The Environmental Food Ccrisis—The Environment's Role in Averting Future Food Crises. A UNEP rapid response assessment*. Arendal, Norway: United Nations Environment Programme.

Neumayer, Eric, and Thomas Plümper. 2007. The Gendered Nature of Natural Disasters: The Impact of Catastrophic Events on the Gender Gap in Life Expectancy, 1981–2002. *Annals of the American Association of Geographers* 97(3): 551–566.

Nichter, Mark. 2003. Smoking: What Does Culture Have to Do with It? *Addiction* 98 (suppl. 1): 139–145.

———. 2008. *Global Health: Why Cultural Perceptions, Social Representations, and Biopolitics Matter.* Tucson: The University of Arizona Press.

Nichter, Mark, and Mimi Nichter. 1996. Health Social Science Research on the Study of Diarrheal Disease: A Focus on Dysentery. In *Anthropology and International Health: Asian Case Studies*, Mark Nichter and Mimi Nichter (eds.), pp. 111–134. Amsterdam, The Netherlands: Overseas Publishers Association.

Nicogossian, A., T. Zimmerman, O. Kloiber, A. Grigoriev, N. Koizumi, J. Heineman-Pieper, J. Mayer, C. Doarn, and W. Jacobs. 2011. Disaster Medicine: The Need for Global Action. *World Medical and Health Policy* 3(1): Article 1.

NIH News. 2005, March 16. Obesity Threatens to Cut U.S. Life Expectancy, New Analysis Suggests. Available online at: at http://www.nih.gov/news/pr/mar2005/nia-16.htm. Accessed 6/15/12.

Nonini, Donald. 2007. *The Global Idea of "the Commons."* New York: Berghahn.

Nordstrom, Carolyn. 1997. *A Different Kind of War Story.* Philadelphia: University of Pennsylvania Press.

———. 2004. *Shadows of War: Violence, Power, and International Profiteering in the Twenty-First Century.* Berkeley: University of California Press.

Noyes, P., M. McElwee, H. Miller, B. Clark, L. Van Tiem, K. Walcott, K. Erins, and E. Levin. 2009. The Toxicology of Climate Change: Environmental Contaminants in a Warming World. *Environment International* 35: 971–986.

Office of the United Nations High Commissioner for Refugees. 2009. *UNHCR Annual Report*. New York: United Nations. Available online at: http://www.unhcr.org/4af2f0f29.html. Accessed 9/13/12.

———. 2010. Sixty Years and Still Counting: *UNHCR Global Trends*. Geneva, Switzerland. United Nations High Commissioner for Refugees. Available online at: http://www.unhcr.org/4dfa11499.pdf. Accessed 9/13/12.

Oliver-Smith, Anthony. 2009. Climate Change and Population Displacement: Disasters and Diasporas in the Twenty-First Century. In *Anthropology and Climate Change: From Encounters to Actions*. Susan Crate, and Mark Nuttall (eds.), pp. 116–136. Walnut Creek, CA: Left Coast Press.

Orlove, Ben, and Seven Caton. 2010. Water Sustainability: Anthropological Approaches and Prospects. *Annual Reviews in Anthropology* 39: 401–415.

Pace, David. 2005. More Blacks Live With Pollution. Associated Press release December 13. New York: Associated Press.

Pan American Health Organization. 2012. *Paho Technical Advisory Group on Vaccine-preventable Disease*. Washington, DC: PAHO.

Parker, Audrey. 2009. War on Water: A Clash over Oil, Power and Poverty in the Niger Delta. *Global Policy Forum*. Available online at: http://www.globalpolicy.org/security-council/dark-side-of-natural-resources/oil-and-natural-gas-in-conflict/africa/49004.html. Accessed 7/13/11.

Paul, Benjamin. 1955. Introduction: Understanding the Community. In *Health, Culture and Community: Case Studies of Public Reactions to Health Programs*, Benjamin Paul (ed.), pp. 1–11. New York: Russell Sage Foundation.

Pedersen, Jon. 2009. *Health and Conflict: A Review of the Links*. Oslo: Fafo.

Pope, C. 2000. Epidemiology of Fine Particulate Air pollution and Human Health: Biologic Mechanisms and Who's at Risk? *Environmental Health Perspectives* 108 (Supplement 4): 713–723.

Pottier, Johan. 1999. Anthropology *of Food: The Social Dynamics of Food Security*. Malden, MA: Blackwell.

Prüss-Üstün, A., and C. Corvalán. 2006. *Preventing Disease Through Healthy Environments: Towards an Estimate of the Environment Burden of Disease*. Geneva, Switzerland: World Health Organization.

Qian, Z., Q. He, H. Lin, L. Kong, C. Bentley, and W. Liu. 2008. High Temperatures Enhanced Acute Mortality Effects of Ambient Particle Pollution in the "Oven" City of Wuhan, China. *Environmental Health Perspectives* 116: 1172–1178.

Quisumbing, Agnes R., Lynn R. Brown, Hilary S. Feldstein, Lawrence Haddad, and Christin Peña. 1995. Women: The Key to Food Security. *Food Policy Statement 21*. Washington, DC: International Food Policy Research Institute.

Renne, Elisha. 2006. Perspectives on Polio and Immunization in Northern Nigeria. *Social Science and Medicine* 63: 1857–1869.

Rosegrant, Mark, Ximing Cai, and Sarah Cline. 2002. *Global Water Outlook to 2025: Averting an Impending Crisis*. Washington, DC: International Food Policy Research Institute.

Rosenzweig, C., W. Solecki, R. Blake, M. Bowman, C. Faris, V. Gornitz, R. Horton, K. Jacob, A. LeBlanc, R. Leichenko, M. Linkin, D. Major, M. O'Grady, L. Patrick, E. Sussman, G. Yohe, G. and R. Zimmerman. 2011. Developing Coastal Adaptation to Climate Change in the New York City Infrastructure-Shed: Process, Approach, Tools, and Strategies. *Climatic Change* 106: 93–127.

Rosing, Howard. 2012. Economic Restructuring and Urban Food Access in the Dominican Republic. *NAPA Bulletin* 32: 55–76.

Ruddiman, William. 2005. *Plows, Plagues, and Petroleum: How Humans Took Control of Climate*. Princeton, NJ: Princeton University Press.

Ryan, Orla. 2008. Food Rights Grip Haiti. *The Guardian*. Available online at: http://www.guardian.co.uk/world/2008/apr/09/11. Accessed 2/29/12.

Saethre, Eirik. 2011. Demand Sharing, Nutrition and Warlpiri Health: The Social and Economic Strategies of Food Choice. In *Ethnography and the Production of Anthropological Knowledge: Essays in Honour of Nicolas*

Peterson, Yasmine Musharbash and Marcus Barber (eds.), pp. 175–186. Canberra, Australia: Australian National University Press.

San Martín, José, Olivia Brathwaite, Betzana Zambrano, José Solórzano, Alain Bouckenooghe, Gustavo Dayan, and María Guzmán. 2010. The Epidemiology of Dengue in the Americas Over the Last Three Decades: A Worrisome Reality. *American Journal of Tropical Medicine and Hygiene* 82(1): 128–135.

Scheper-Hughes, Nancy. 1992. *Death without Weeping: The Violence of Everyday Life in Brazil*. Berkeley: University of California Press.

Schjolden, Ane. 2000. *Leather Tanning in India: Environmental Regulations and Firms' Compliance*. Oslo: University of Oslo FIL Programme.

Schoepf, Brook, Claude Schoepf, and Joyce Millen. 2000. Theoretical Therapies, Remote Remedies: SAPs and the Political Ecology of Poverty and Health in Africa. In *Dying for Growth: Global Inequality and the Health of the Poor*, Jim Yong Kim, Joyce Millen, Alec Irwin, and John Gershman (eds.), pp. 91–125. Monroe, Maine: Common Courage Press.

Schowengerdt, Anna, Paul Spiegel, and Fred Spielberg. 1998. Health Interventions in Complex Emergencies: A Case Study of Liberia. World Health Organization. Available online at: http://www.who.int/hac/techguidance/training/analysing_health_systems/liberia_health_interventions_complex_emergencies.pdf. Accessed 6/11/11.

Scrimshaw, Nevin, and John Paul San Giovanni. 1997. Synergism of Nutrition, Infection and Immunity. *American Journal of Clinical Nutrition* 66: 464S–477S.

Scudder, T., and E. Colson. 1982. From Welfare to Development: A Conceptual Framework for the Analysis of Dislocated People. In *Involuntary Migration and Resettlement*. A. Hansen and A. Oliver-Smith, A. (eds.), p. 267–287. Boulder, CO: Westview Press.

Sen, Amartya. 1981. *Poverty and Famines: An Essay on Entitlement and Deprivation*. Oxford, UK: Oxford University Press

Sharkey, Patrick. 2007. Survival and Death in New Orleans: An Empirical Look at the Human Impact of Hurricane Katrina. *Journal of Black Studies* 37: 482–550.

Shiva, Vandana. 1991. The Green Revolution in the Punjab. *The Ecologists* 21(2). Available online at: http://livingheritage.org/green-revolution.htm. Accessed 3/1/12.

———. 2002. *Water Wars: Privatization, Pollution, and Profit*. Boston: South End Press.

Sidibé, Michel. 2011. Securing the Future of Global Health—The Role of the G20. *The G20 and Sustainable Healthcare*. Available online at: http://healthg20.com/wp-content/uploads/2011/11/24-33-Michel-Sidib%C3%A9.pdf. Accessed 3/5/12.

Simonsen, L., M. Dalton, R. Breiman, T. Hennessy, E. Umland, C. Sewell, P. Rollin, T. Ksiazek, and C. Peters. 1995. Evaluation of the Magnitude of the 1993 Hantavirus Outbreak in the Southwestern United States. *Journal of Infectious Diseases* 172(3): 729–733.

Singer, Merrill. 2008a. *Drugging the Poor: Legal and Illegal Drug Industries and the Structuring of Social Inequality*. Long Grove, IL: Waveland Press.

———. 2008b. *Drugs and Development: Global Impact on Sustainable Growth and Human Rights*. Long Grove, IL: Waveland Press.

———. 2009a. Beyond Global Warming: Interacting Ecocrises and the Critical Anthropology of Health. *Anthropology Quarterly* 82(3): 795–820.

———. 2009b. *Introduction to Syndemics: A Systems Approach to Public and Community Health*. San Francisco, CA: Jossey-Bass.

———. 2010. Atmospheric and Marine Pluralea Interactions and Species Extinction Risks. *Journal of Cosmology* 8: 1832–1837.

———. 2011a. Down Cancer Alley: The Lived Experience of Health and Environmental Suffering in Louisiana's Chemical Corridor. *Medical Anthropology Quarterly* 25(2): 141–163.

———. 2011b. Toward a Critical Biosocial Model of Ecohealth in Southern Africa: The HIV/AIDS and Nutrition Insecurity Syndemic. *Annals of Anthropology Practice* 36(1): 8–27.

Singer, Merrill, and Hans Baer. 2009. *Killer Commodities: Public Health and the Corporate Production of Harm*. Lanham, MD: AltaMira.

Singer, Merrill C., Pamela I. Erickson, Louise Badiane, Rosemary Diaz, Dugeidy Ortiz, Traci Abraham, and Anna Marie Nicolaysen. 2006. Syndemics, Sex, and the City: Understanding Sexually Transmitted Diseases in Social and Cultural Context. *Social Science and Medicine* 63(8): 2010–2021.

Singer, Merrill, and G. Derrick Hodge, Eds. 2010. *The War Machine and Global Health*. Lanham, MD: AltaMira.

Sivard, Ruth. 1996. *World Military and Social Expenditures*. Washington, DC: World Priorities.

Smith, Stephen. 2012. The Triple Threat of Unstable Food Prices. *World Ark*, February, pp. 13–21.

Smith-Morris, Carolyn. 2008. *Diabetes among the Pima: Stories of Survival*. Tucson: University of Arizona Press.

Stanley, David. 2007. South Pacific Organizer: Tuvalu. Available online at: http://www.southpacific.org/faq/tuvalu.html. Accessed 5/21/11.

Stebbins, Kenyon. 2001. Going like Gangbusters. Transnational Tobacco Companies "Making a Killing" in South America. *Medical Anthropology Quarterly* 15: 147–170.

Stein, Eric. 2009. "Sanitation Makeshifts" and the Perpetuation of Health Stratification in Indonesia. In *Anthropology and Public Health: Bridging Differences in Culture and Society*, Robert Hahn and Marcia Inhorn (eds.), pp. 541–565. Oxford, UK: Oxford University Press.

Swaminathan, Madhura. 1996. Structural Adjustment, Food Security and System of Public Distribution of Food. *Economic and Political Weekly* 31(26): 1665–1672.

Sweetland, A., J. Acha, and D. Guerra. 2002. Enhancing Adherence: The role of Group Psychotherapy in the Treatment of MDR-TB in Urban Peru. In *World Mental Health Casebook*, A. Cohen, A. Kleinman, B. Saraceno (eds.), pp. 51–79. New York: Kluwer Academic/Plenum.

Szabo, Liz. 2011. Study finds toxic chemicals in pregnant women's bodies. *USA Today*. Available online at: http://www.usatoday.com/yourlife/parenting-family/pregnancy/2011-01-14-chemicals14_st_N.htm?csp=34news. Accessed 5/27/11.

Thill, Scott. 2008. Africa: The Next Victim in Our Quest for Cheap Oil. *Third World Traveler*. Available online at: http://www.thirdworldtraveler.com/Africa/Africa_Victim_Oil.html. Accessed 7/13/11.

Toole, Michael, and Ronald Waldman. 1990. Prevention of Excess Mortality in Refugee and Displaced Populations in Developing Countries. *Journal of the American Medical Association* 263(24): 3296–3302.

Tylor, Edward. 1871. *Primitive Culture*. New York: J. P. Putnam's Sons.

UN News Centre. 2011. Remarks to General Assembly Thematic Debate on Investment in and Financing of Productive Capacities of Least developed Countries. Available online at: http://www.un.org/apps/news/infocus/sgspeeches/search_full.asp?statID=1102. Accessed 5/27/11.

UNICEF. 2000. The Progress of Nations 2000. Available online at: http://www.unicef.org/pon00/pon2000.pdf. Accessed 5/27/11.

United Nations. 1948. Universal Declaration of Human Rights. Available online at: http://www.un.org/en/documents/udhr/. Accessed 4/3/12.

———. 2005. *Children Under Threat: The State of the World's Children*. Geneva, Switzerland.

United Nations Atlas of the Oceans. 2010. Human Settlements on the Coast. Available online at http://www.oceansatlas.org/servlet/CDSServlet?status=ND0xODc3JjY9ZW4mMzM9KiYzNz1rb3M~. Accessed 2/11/12.

United Nations Development Programme. 2006. Beyond Scarcity: Power, Poverty and the Global Water Crisis. *Human Development Report 2006*. New York: Human Development Report Office.

United Nations Millennium Ecosystem Assessment. 2007. Millennium Assessment Reports. Available online at: http://www.maweb.org/en/index.aspx. Accessed 5/27/11.

United Nations Office for the Coordination of Humanitarian Affairs. 2008. *Natural Disasters and Forced Displacement in the Context of Climate Change*. Geneva, Switzerland: OCHA.

United Nations Office of Drugs and Crime. 2006. *World Drug Report*. Geneva, Switzerland.

United Nations System Standing Committee of Nutrition. 2004. *5th Report on the World Nutrition Situation: Nutrition for Improved Development Outcomes*. Geneva, Switzerland: UNSCN Secretariat.

US Census Bureau. 2011. *Income, Poverty and Health Insurance Coverage in the United States: 2010*. Available online at: http://www.census.gov/prod/2011pubs/p60-239.pdf. Accessed 9/13/12.

Üstün, T. Bedirhan. 1999. The Global Burden of Mental Disorders. *American Journal of Public Health* 89: 1315–1318.

Valent, F., D. Little, R. Bertollini, L. Nemer, F. Barbone, and G. Tamburlini. 2004. Burden of Disease Attributable to Selected Environmental Factors and Injury among Children and Adolescents in Europe. *Lancet* 363: 2032–2039.

Vidal, John. 2010. Nigeria's Agony Dwarfs the Gulf Oil Spill. The US and Europe Ignore It. *The Observer*, May 10. Available online at: http://www.guardian.co.uk/world/2010/may/30/oil-spills-nigeria-niger-delta-shell. Accessed 7/13/11.

Wainwright, Joel. 2008. *Decolonizing Development: Colonial Power and the Maya*. Malden, MA: Blackwell.

Waters, Malcolm. 2001. *Globalization*. London: Routledge.

Watkins, Kevin. 2006. Beyond Scarcity: Power, Poverty and the Global Water Crisis. *Human Development Report, 2006*. New York: United Nations Development Programme. Available online at: http://hdr.undp.org/en/media/Forword_Acknowledgements_Content.pdf. Accessed 9/13/12.

Weisfield-Adams, Emma. 2008. *Factsheet: Woman Farmers and Food Security.* New York: Hunger Project.

Wellen, Edward. 1955. Water Boiling in a Peruvian Town. In *Health, Culture and Community: Case Studies of Public Reactions to Health Programs,* Benjamin Paul (ed.), pp. 71–103. New York: Russell Sage Foundation.

White, Nancy. 2006. A Toxic Life. *The Toronto Star,* April 21. Available online at: http://yourhealthandmine.net/toxinsenv7.htm. Accessed 5/31/11.

Whiteford, Linda, and Lenore Manderson. 2000. *Global Health Policy, Local Realities.* Boulder, CO: Lynne Rienner.

Whiteford, Linda, and Cecilia Vindrola Padros. 2011. The Medical Anthropology of Water. In *A Companion to Medical Anthropology.* Merrill Singer, Pamela I. Erickson (eds.), pp. 197–218. Malden, MA: Blackwell.

Whiteford, Linda, and Scott Whiteford, Eds. 2005. *Globalization, Water, and Health: Resource Management in Times of Scarcity.* Santa Fe: School of American Research Press.

WHO (World Health Organization). 1981. *Global Strategy for Health for All by the Year 2000.* Geneva, Switzerland: WHO

———. 1998. *Health Sector Emergency Preparedness Guide.* Geneva, Switzerland: WHO.

———. 2001. Confronting the Tobacco Epidemic in an Era of Trade Liberalization. Geneva, Switzerland: WHO.

———. 2002. The World Health Report, 2002: Reducing Risks, Promoting Healthy Life. *Bangladesh Development Series, Paper # 12.* Dhaka, Bangladesh: World Health Organization.

———. 2004a. *Dengue: Burdens and Trends.* Geneva, Switzerland: WHO.

———. 2004b. WHO Launches Plan to Jointly Fight TB and HIV. Available online at: http://www.afro.who.int/en/media-centre/pressreleases/544-who-launches-plan-to-jointly-fight-tb-and-hiv.html. Accessed 5/30/11.

———. 2005a. Ecosystem and Human Well-being: Health Synthesis. Geneva, Switzerland: WHO.

———. 2005b. Mental Health: Facing the Challenges, Building Solutions. Report from the WHO European Ministerial Conference. Copenhagen, Denmark: WHO Regional Office for Europe.

———. 2005c. *Water for Life: Making it Happen.* Geneva, Switzerland: WHO/UNICEF Joint Monitoring Programme for Water Supply and Sanitation.

———. 2007. Fact Sheet No. 310. The Top Ten Causes of Death. Available online at http://www.who.int/mediacentre/factsheets/fs310.pdf. Accessed 3/4/12.

———. 2008. Closing the Gap in a Generation: Health Equity through Action on the Social Determinants of Health. *Final Report of the Commission on Social Determinants of Health.* Geneva, Switzerland: WHO.

———. 2009. Statement—WHO Working Group on Urogenital Schistosomiasis and HIV Transmission. Available online at: http://www.who.int/neglected_diseases/integrated_media_urogenital_schistosomiasis/en/index.html. Accessed 6/10/11.

———. 2011a. WHO Report on the Global Tobacco Epidemic, 2011: Warning about the Dangers of Tobacco. Geneva, Switzerland.

———. 2011b. Tobacco Fact Sheet Number 339. Available online at: http://www.who.int/mediacentre/factsheets/fs339/en/index.html. Accessed 7/14/11.

———. 2011c. Global Health Observatory Data Repository, Country Statistics—Haiti. Available online at: http://apps.who.int/ghodata/?vid=10000&theme=country. Accessed 5/20/11.

———. 2012. Maternal Mortality Fact Sheet Number 348. Available online at: http://www.who.int/mediacentre/factsheets/fs348/en/index.html. Accessed 9/13/12.

World Bank. 2006. Bangladesh: Country Environmental Analysis. *Bangladesh Development Series Paper No: 12*. Washington, DC, and Dhaka, Bangladesh: The World Bank. Available online at: http://siteresources.worldbank.org/BANGLADESHEXTN/Resources/295759-1173922647418/complete.pdf. Accessed 9/13/12.

———. 2012. How We Classify Countries. Available online at: http://data.worldbank.org/about/country-classifications. Accessed 10/19/12.

World Business Council for Sustainable Development. 2011. Water. Available online at: http://www.wbcsd.org/work-program/sector-projects/water.aspx. Accessed 2/20/2012.

World Food Program. 2012. Hunger Stats. Available online at: http://www.wfp.org/hunger/stats. Accessed 2/22/12.

World Wildlife Federation-UK. 1999. *Chemical Trespass: A Toxic Legacy–Executive Summary.* Available online at: http://www.wwf.org.uk/filelibrary/pdf/chem4.pdf. Accessed 5/27/11.

World Wildlife Fund. 2003. *Managing Rivers Wisely: Lessons from WWF's Work for Integrated River Basin Management*. Gland, Switzerland: WWF.

Yong Kim, Jim, Aaron Shakow, Kedar Mate, Chris Vanderwarker, Rajesh Gupta, and Paul Farmer. 2005. Limited Good and Limited Vision: Multidrug-Resistant Tuberculosis and Global Health Policy. *Social Science and Medicine* 61(4): 847–859.

Young, I., S. Zieger, and A. Babanin. 2011. Global Trends in Wind Speed and Wave Height. *Science* 332(6028): 451–455.

Zhang, Y., W. Huang, S. London, G. Song, G. Chen, and L. Jiang. 2006. Ozone and Daily Mortality in Shanghai, China. *Environmental Health Perspectives* 114: 1227–1232.

Web Resources

A short but vital list of Web resources on global health includes:

1. World Health Organization: http://www.who.int/en/
2. U.S. Department of Health and Human Service: Global Health Program: http://www.GlobalHealth.gov
3. Centers for Disease Control and Prevention, Global Health: http://www.cdc.gov/GlobalHealth/
4. UNICEF: http://www.unicef.org
5. Pan American Health Organization: http://www.paho.org
6. The Global Fund: http://www.theglobalfund.org
7. Global Health Magazine: http://www.globalhealthmagazine.com/
8. Union of Concerned Scientists: http://www.ucsusa.org/
9. International Women's Health Coalition: http://www.iwhc.org/
10. Millennium Development Goals: http://www.un.org/millenniumgoals/

Index